The Teacher Journal

The Teacher Journal

Naomi Barker

BLOOMSBURY EDUCATION

LONDON OXFORD NEW YORK NEW DELHI SYDNEY

BLOOMSBURY EDUCATION
Bloomsbury Publishing Plc
50 Bedford Square, London, WC1B 3DP, UK
29 Earlsfort Terrace, Dublin 2, Ireland

BLOOMSBURY, BLOOMSBURY EDUCATION and the Diana logo
are trademarks of Bloomsbury Publishing Plc

First published in in Great Britain, 2022 by Bloomsbury Publishing Plc
This edition published in Great Britain, 2022 by Bloomsbury Publishing Plc

A catalogue record for this book is available from the British Library

ISBN: PB: 978-1-8019-9031-8; ePDF: 978-1-8019-9030-1

2 4 6 8 10 9 7 5 3 1

Text design by Jeni Child

Printed and bound in the UK by CPI Group Ltd, CR0 4YY

MIX
Paper from
responsible sources
FSC® C013604

To find out more about our authors and books visit www.bloomsbury.com
and sign up for our newsletters

To Ava-Rose

*I would like to thank all the students I have taught who have brought me so much joy in my work
over the years. Further thanks to my many brilliant colleagues who have helped me to grow
professionally through all their guidance and shared wisdom. Finally, thank you to my own
support network, especially my husband for his unwavering belief in me.*

Naomi Barker

Contents

Introduction

Recently, an old acquaintance got in touch to ask me about my work. He said that he had considered teaching as a new career path but was concerned about what it involved. A mutual friend, in a bid to give him a positive perspective, had told him to contact me. 'So I've heard you think it's actually pretty great?' he asked. It was with pleasure that I could say with honesty, that 'Yes, it is brilliant'. That doesn't mean to say it isn't tough at times, but part of that challenge is what makes it the most privileged position to undertake. Sometimes we don't hear this enough. As practitioners, we don't always have a chance to appreciate it, given the quantity of demands the role can have. I'm hoping that this journal will be one route to alleviating this.

This is the book I wish I had when I was starting out. My vision is that the support it offers will encourage more of my esteemed colleagues to remain passionate about the profession, paired with continued opportunities to develop as a practitioner.

You are about to enter a brilliant career where every day you will be making a difference to the wonderful individuals who are your students. I hope that this journal gives you some measure of that impact and helps to remind you of not only why you chose this pathway but of how you can flourish within it.

A guide to using this journal

You are about to embark on your journey as an early career teacher (ECT), an incredibly exciting venture. This is a journal designed to support you through this as a supplement to the induction programme you will be receiving in school. It can be used to record your weekly thoughts, feelings and ideas through a series of reflective pieces, questions and activities along with space for your own notes. Consider it to be both the cheerleader and assistant to your teaching year. However, it simply provides a structure to your thoughts – you are creating the content in response. The aim is to empower you to reflect on the incredible work you already do and the steps you can take to cultivate your professional growth, whilst also prioritising wellbeing and self-care. To facilitate this process, the journal is structured as follows:

1 The journal starts with a reflection on both the professional and personal journey you will be undertaking with a view to best practice and wellbeing. This includes space for you to record appraisal targets and relevant evidence in relation to your development as preparation for your professional reviews and formal assessment.

To help with this, a table cross-referencing the journal reflection points against the Teachers' Standards (DfE, 2021a) has been provided on page 14.

2 The journal moves on to a guided preparation section to help with the transition into being an ECT, beginning with an opportunity to engage with school context. Ideally, this should be completed before the start of the new academic year. This is a chance to research and prepare accordingly for your given institution's context, which will help inform your practice. There is also space to record your checklist of essential items to have ready in advance – some suggestions are provided.

3 The journal itself is structured around each week of the school year. There is a weekly piece relating to wellbeing and/or professional development. These guided reflections signpost next steps for engaging with the ideas presented and there is space to record your thoughts and action points. Where relevant, the text indicates with a 'sticker' how your cogitations can act as evidence towards the Teachers' Standards as set out in the table on page 14.

There is space every week to write down your favourite student quote and highlight of the week. These are those frequent moments in teaching which are so precious and yet easily forgotten in a busy week. Highlights are not prescribed but can be anything personal to you – examples could include a moment in a lesson or a positive conversation you've had. Just remember, there is no 'right' response!

Having the opportunity to make a note of these highlights will hopefully allow you to capture some of the best parts of working with young people across an academic year. Furthermore, in more trying moments, being able to then return to these highlights will help remind you to celebrate and take confidence in the excellent work you have done and hopefully serve to motivate you as an example of why working with young people is so special. For the same reason, you may want to consider keeping any cards or messages that you receive across the year in a safe place.

A series of pedagogical thematic 'Think pieces' summarising key research and practical strategies feature throughout the journal. These are directly linked to both the Early Career Framework (ECF) and Teachers' Standards. Your engagement with these is specifically focused on helping to facilitate best practice and your writing and action points can be used as part of your induction evidence-collection process.

The reflection tasks do not necessarily have to be done straight away. In fact, many of the follow-up points might benefit from being completed over a period of time so that you have a fuller portfolio for embedding and evaluating how effective you have found a given technique or strategy. Part of these reflections includes a recommendation to observe excellent practice within a specific area. To help with organising these, it is advisable to discuss the Think piece with your in-school mentor when you meet so that they can help you co-ordinate your observation with an appropriate member of staff.

Section 8 of the ECF under 'Professional Behaviours' states – 'reflective practice, supported by feedback from and observation of experienced colleagues, professional debate, and learning from educational research, is also likely to support improvement' (DfE, 2019a, p. 24). It is worth noting that these Think pieces are designed to help contribute towards this aim whilst remaining intentionally brief so that they provide an accessible insight into promoting classroom pedagogy within the demands of a working week. However, hopefully they act as a platform for your own further exploration of the ideas or strategies presented during your in-school induction and, when your own time allows, the bibliography at the end of this journal can help as a starting point, too.

Your professional journey

Starting at a school as an ECT can feel daunting, but it is important to remember how much you have already achieved. Completing teacher training is a challenging process and not only have you managed this, but you have also secured a job. Clearly there is much that you have already accomplished, and you should feel confident about your abilities.

What is particularly exciting about a teacher's journey is that professional development as an educator is lifelong. A great practitioner is one who constantly strives to improve their impact on students' learning (Coe et al., 2020, p.10). Your period as an ECT is an invaluable opportunity to develop your teaching with additional support and to embed the mindset of a reflective individual who is constantly looking to better themselves.

Reflections

Reflect on your professional journey so far. What are you proudest of? Perhaps it was a student you won round, a technique you refined or a development point you made great progress with.

Across the academic year you will have two professional progress reviews with your induction tutor. The conversation will be 'informed by existing evidence' and will be an opportunity to 'review the ECT's progress against the Teachers' Standards' (DfE, 2021b, p. 22). You will be entitled to a written record of this meeting, and it will include a summary of the evidence and the 'agreed development targets… It is also expected that objectives are reviewed and revised in relation to the Teachers' Standards and the needs and strengths of the individual ECT' (DfE, 2021b, p. 22).

In your final term, you will have a formal assessment which again you will need to provide evidence for. This does not involve creating new work but rather drawing on what you already have in place from across the academic year. A formal assessment report will be completed which includes a judgement of your progress against the Teachers' Standards (note not the ECF – more on this to follow).

Reflections

Look back to the end of your training year and your appraisal targets. Make a note of these in the targets table on page 14 – they provide a starting point for your continued professional progress this academic year. This table can be returned to at relevant points as a central space to record and monitor your targets following your reviews.

Now consider how they might frame your developmental targets for this year. Reflect on which areas of practice you feel you would benefit from focusing on and what support you might require to help with your growth. It will be useful to bring this to your first meeting with your induction tutor and mentor.

Record of appraisal and developmental targets

	Appraisal & developmental targets
Start of the academic year	
Autumn professional progress review	
Spring professional progress review	
Summer formal assessment	

Review of targets/notes

Tracking your progress against the Teachers' Standards

The Teachers' Standards as set out by the Department for Education (2021a) are an essential component of your ECT progress reviews and formal assessment. 'The standards define the minimum level of practice expected of trainees and teachers from the point of being awarded QTS' (DfE, 2021a, p. 6) and will be used to assess your performance across your induction period in school (DfE, 2021b, p. 6). They work in congruence with the ECF, but the framework itself is not a tool for assessment. Rather, the Department for Education describes the ECF as a 'platform for future development' which 'builds on and complements' initial teacher training (2019a, p. 5). Your school will cover the 'learn about' and 'learn how to do' elements it details in greater depth as part of your induction programme. This journal complements this provision.

Record of progress against Teachers' Standards

Teachers' Standards reference	Corresponding section in the ECF	Relevant journal sections and pages
Part 1: Teaching		
1. Set high expectations which inspire, motivate and challenge pupils	1. High expectations	**Think piece 1:** Expectations (p. 44)
		Think piece 2: Behaviour management (p. 52)
		Think piece 7: Mindsets (p. 92)
		Think piece 10: Adaptive teaching (p. 122)
		Autumn 1 Week 1: Researching your classes (p. 40)
		Autumn 1 Week 2: Meeting your classes (p. 42)

The Teachers' Standards table below is designed to help with your professional development, highlighting where your guided reflections or Think pieces link back to both the Teachers' Standards and the ECF. The Reflection pieces throughout the journal have references to the Teachers' Standards, apart from those that are wellbeing focused. This will allow you to easily track your progress, develop and collate your evidence across an academic year with space to add your own notes as you continue to work towards these standards. The table can therefore be used to inform your reviews and assessments as captured in the targets table on page 12. As a central record of evidence for your progress, it is advisable to bring it to these meetings with the relevant accompanying documentation, such as lesson observation records (of both yourself and others).

Additional evidence collected/notes

Teachers' Standards reference	Corresponding section in the ECF	Relevant journal sections and pages
		Autumn 1 Week 5: Managing relationships with students and staff (p. 50)
		Autumn 1 Week 6: Safeguarding (p. 54)
		Autumn 2 Week 4: Communicating with parents, carers and guardians (p. 70)
		Spring 1 Week 1: Re-establishing your expectations (p. 82)
		Spring 1 Week 5: Metacognition (p. 94)
		Summer 1 Week 1: Reflecting on highlights (p. 118)
		Summer 1 Week 2: Teaching lessons outside your subject area (p. 120)
		Summer 1 Week 6: Half-termly reflections (3) (p. 132)
2. Promote good progress and outcomes by pupils	**2. How pupils learn**	**Think piece 3:** Scaffolding (p. 62)
		Think piece 5: Feedback (p. 72)
		Think piece 6: Responsive teaching (p. 86)
		Think piece 7: Mindsets (p. 92)
		Think piece 8: Retrieval practice (p. 102)
		Think piece 9: Cognitive load (p. 110)
		Think piece 12: Literacy (p. 138)
		Autumn 1 Week 1: Researching your classes (p. 40)
		Autumn 2 Week 5: Making marking meaningful (p. 74)
		Spring 1 Week 5: Metacognition (p. 94)
		Spring 2 Week 3: Homework (p. 106)

Additional evidence collected/notes

Teachers' Standards reference	Corresponding section in the ECF	Relevant journal sections and pages
		Spring 2 Week 4: Making use of technology (p. 108)
		Spring 2 Week 5: Use of group work (p. 112)
3. Demonstrate good subject and curriculum knowledge	3. Subject and curriculum	**Think piece 1:** Expectations (p. 44)
		Think piece 3: Scaffolding (p. 62)
		Think piece 4: Subject and curriculum knowledge (p. 68)
		Think piece 8: Retrieval practice (p. 102)
		Think piece 9: Cognitive load (p. 110)
		Think piece 12: Literacy (p. 138)
		Autumn 2 Week 3: Collaborative departmental planning (p. 66)
		Spring 1 Week 5: Metacognition (p. 94)
		Summer 1 Week 5: Curriculum planning for the future (p. 130)
4. Plan and teach well-structured lessons	4. Classroom practice	**Think piece 1:** Expectations (p. 44)
		Think piece 3: Scaffolding (p. 62)
		Think piece 4: Subject and curriculum knowledge (p. 68)
		Think piece 5: Feedback (p. 72)
		Think piece 6: Responsive teaching (p. 86)
		Think piece 7: Mindsets (p. 92)
		Think piece 8: Retrieval practice (p. 102)
		Think piece 9: Cognitive load (p. 110)

Additional evidence collected/notes

Teachers' Standards reference	Corresponding section in the ECF	Relevant journal sections and pages
		Think piece 11: Dialogic talk and questioning (p. 128)
		Autumn 2 Week 3: Collaborative departmental planning (p. 66)
		Spring 1 Week 4: Observations and feedback on your practice (p. 90)
		Spring 1 Week 5: Metacognition (p. 94)
		Spring 2 Week 3: Homework (p. 106)
		Spring 2 Week 5: Use of group work (p. 112)
		Summer 1 Week 5: Curriculum planning for the future (p. 130)
5. Adapt teaching to respond to the strengths and needs of all pupils	5. Adaptive teaching	**Think piece 6:** Responsive teaching (p. 86)
		Think piece 9: Cognitive load (p. 110)
		Think piece 10: Adaptive teaching (p. 122)
		Think piece 12: Literacy (p. 138)
		Autumn 1 Week 1: Researching your classes (p. 40)
		Spring 2 Week 3: Homework (p. 106)
6. Make accurate and productive use of assessment	6. Assessment	**Think piece 5:** Feedback (p. 72)
		Think piece 6: Responsive teaching (p. 86)
		Think piece 8: Retrieval practice (p. 102)
		Autumn 2 Week 5: Making marking meaningful (p. 74)
		Spring 2 Week 3: Homework (p. 106)

Additional evidence collected/notes

Teachers' Standards reference	Corresponding section in the ECF	Relevant journal sections and pages
7. Manage behaviour effectively to ensure a good and safe learning environment	7. Managing behaviour	**Think piece 1:** Expectations (p. 44)
		Think piece 2: Behaviour management (p. 52)
		Autumn 1 Week 1: Researching your classes (p. 40)
		Autumn 1 Week 2: Meeting your classes (p. 42)
		Autumn 1 Week 5: Managing relationships with students and staff (p. 50)
		Autumn 2 Week 4: Communicating with parents, carers and guardians (p. 70)
		Summer 1 Week 1: Reflecting on highlights (p. 118)
		Summer 1 Week 2: Teaching lessons outside your subject area (p. 120)
		Summer 1 Week 6: Half-termly reflections (3) (p. 132)
8. Fulfil wider professional responsibilities	8. Professional behaviours	**Think piece 7:** Mindsets (p. 92)
		Think piece 10: Adaptive teaching (p. 122)
		Autumn 1 Week 1: Researching your classes (p. 40)
		Autumn 1 Week 5: Managing relationships with students and staff (p. 50)
		Autumn 1 Week 6: Safeguarding (p. 54)
		Autumn 1 Week 7: Half-termly reflections (1) (p. 56)
		Autumn 2 Week 1: Reflecting on your professional development (1) (p. 60)
		Autumn 2 Week 4: Communicating with parents, carers and guardians (p. 70)
		Autumn 2 Week 6: Participating in pastoral provision (p. 76)

Additional evidence collected/notes

Teachers' Standards reference	Corresponding section in the ECF	Relevant journal sections and pages
		Autumn 2 Week 7: Revisiting appraisal targets (1) (p. 78)
		Spring 1 Week 2: Extra/Supra-curricular provision (p. 84)
		Spring 1 Week 3: Observations of other staff members (p. 88)
		Spring 1 Week 4: Observations and feedback on your practice (p. 90)
		Spring 1 Week 6: Half-termly reflections (2) (p. 96)
		Spring 2 Week 1: Reflecting on your professional development (2) (p. 100)
		Spring 2 Week 6: Revisiting appraisal targets (2) (p. 114)
		Summer 1 Week 2: Teaching lessons outside your subject area (p. 120)
		Summer 1 Week 3: Coaching (p. 124)
		Summer 1 Week 6: Half-termly reflections (3) (p. 132)
		Summer 2 Week 1: Preparation for formal assessment (p. 136)
		Summer 2 Week 3: Future Continuing Professional Development (CPD) (p. 142)
Part 2: Personal and professional conduct		
		Think piece 2: Behaviour management (p. 52)
		Autumn 1 Week 2: Meeting your classes (p. 42)
		Autumn 1 Week 5: Managing relationships with students and staff (p. 50)
		Autumn 1 Week 6: Safeguarding (p. 54)

Additional evidence collected/notes

Notes

Your personal journey

The new ECT induction programme has been designed to aid the transition from teacher training into working as a qualified professional across a two-year period. This means that you will have both your induction tutor and subject-specific mentor to guide and help you in school, to answer questions and to share any worries or concerns with.

However, it is important to also consider your wider support network – who, outside of school, will be available for you to discuss your experiences with or to reassure and assist you? Ideally you want individuals who will encourage you to be kind to yourself, help you to maintain work/ life boundaries and with whom spending time can give you that well-deserved break from work. Add to your network throughout the year and use it to reach out when you need support. This journal is focused on promoting wellbeing and will support you with the demands of your ECT year.

Reflections

Write a list of the individuals who comprise your wider support network – friends, mentors or family. Return to your list as a reminder of who is available to see and speak to when looking to access support beyond school. Don't hesitate to reach out when it is required.

You need to be honest with yourself about job habits and spend some time reflecting on your ways of working and how these played out during your training programme. This will allow you to then start with an awareness of what helped and where you need to be self-aware of behaviour patterns you might want to challenge.

It is important that you manage your expectations for the year ahead. For example, expecting to have perfectly planned resources for every lesson will likely be at the expense of having much-needed rest and is arguably misguided. High-quality teaching is the greatest resource available in the classroom (Wiliam, 2018, p. 22), not the materials that supplement this offer.

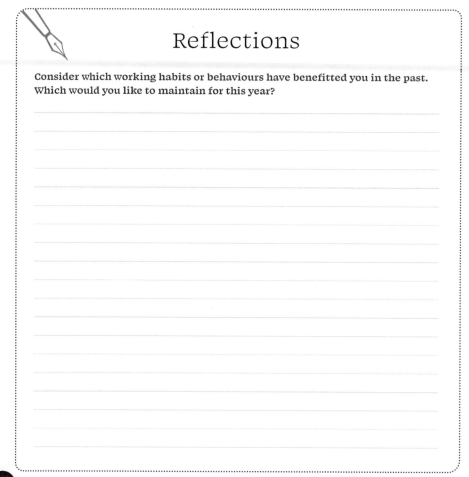

Reflections

Consider which working habits or behaviours have benefitted you in the past. Which would you like to maintain for this year?

Reflections

Which areas have you struggled with and would benefit from revising as you look ahead? For example, this could be around working hours or a drive towards perfectionism. Be honest and try to frame these around your self-care – what helped to promote a comfortable, healthy and happy way of living and which were detrimental to this and need to be adapted?

Use these reflections to set your wellbeing aims for the year ahead on the next page. Ensure that they are positive, achievable goals which you can visualise. For example, perhaps it is to not work past 6 pm on any weekday evening, or to reach out to a member of your support network when you need a boost. The wellbeing hints and tips on page 31 might help as a starting point.

My wellbeing aims

Wellbeing hints and tips

Food

In the rush of a full working week, food can understandably be left as a last-minute thought. However, in reality it ideally needs to be given the same planning and preparation as the other areas of your life. This is the fuel that gets you through your busy day and can impact on mood and energy. Furthermore, sugar can be far too accessible in the school environment, providing the short-term kick without the necessary long-term energy. When possible, try to plan out and prepare your meals so that you include the essential components for a balanced diet. If you have a family to prepare meals for, consider combining preparation for your meals with family meals, or if you want to save time, then the school should have a feasible option in their catering. Equally important is prioritising time in school to stop working and enjoy your food at break and lunch, ideally with colleagues.

Planning activities for outside of working hours

A school has a range of extra and supra-curricular activities which are available to students outside of their core curriculum as a means of enriching their experiences and character. As professionals we can see the value of ensuring that young people are able to engage with this offer. However, sometimes we can lose sight of it for ourselves, particularly in teaching, which can be so consuming, and even more so when we are starting our career. This shouldn't be the case – remember, you are entitled to a life beyond school and maintaining those work boundaries is conducive to staying happy and healthy. Where there are hobbies or activities you enjoy, do continue to prioritise these outside of work. If it is becoming untenable to maintain them alongside work, speak to your mentor so that they can help look at your workload and advise accordingly.

Planning for holidays

The school holidays are essential in teaching as an opportunity to rest and recuperate between intense working terms. Sometimes, planning ahead for these can really help to ensure that you do take the break that is needed from work, and give you that additional motivation on the mornings you are finding it that bit harder to get up. It could be a holiday, a trip, a visit, an activity or just protected time for you which doesn't involve work. Knowing you have something to look forward to in advance can make a difference on those more difficult days.

Understanding your school context

Every school is unique, and understanding the context in which it operates is essential for any teacher starting new at an institution, wherever they are in their career. There are several reasons for this:

1 Empathy is arguably integral to building successful relationships with students. This is not to make undue allowances, but rather to help gain a broader understanding of the background and community which many of the children you teach will come from and how this links with the dynamics and provision of the school.

2 Every school will have a set of values which guides its purpose and provision. It is likely that you familiarised yourself with these core principles prior to even writing your job application. Now is an opportunity to research how these underpin whole-school strategies or approaches that you need to be mindful of when planning. The chances are that your school will already have additional guidance or support available with this which you can look to access.

3 Tailoring the learning to student needs is essential to best practice in education. On a broader scale this begins with the school and then moves down to class and individual levels. Knowing the context of your school is therefore an important starting point for any planning. What may have worked effectively at one of your training schools might not be appropriate in your new setting. Once you begin researching your classes and meeting your students you can make this provision even more bespoke.

Notes

Researching the context of your school

To help learn more about your institution's context, the school's website or staff handbook can be a useful starting point. If it is a state school you can also find relevant information in their last Office for Standards in Education, Children's Services and Skills (OFSTED) report, published on OFSTED's website.

Use your research to answer the following questions and consider how this information might guide your planning for learning:

- What is the status of your school – community, foundation, academy, free, grammar, private or special school? How might this impact on the way that it operates?

- What is the size of your school and how does that compare nationally?

- What is the percentage of disadvantaged students at your school and how does that compare nationally?

- What is the percentage of students with special educational needs and disability (SEND) and how does that compare nationally?

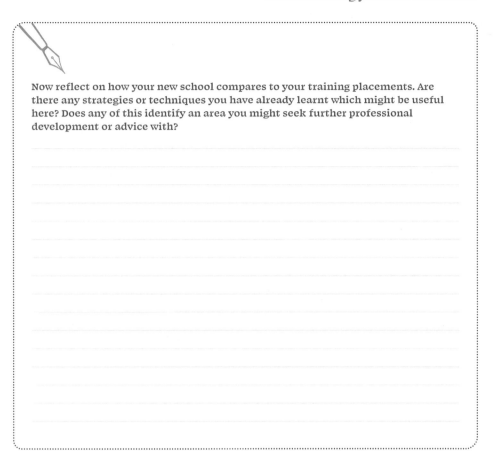

Now reflect on how your new school compares to your training placements. Are there any strategies or techniques you have already learnt which might be useful here? Does any of this identify an area you might seek further professional development or advice with?

Getting to know your school further – next steps

At your initial induction to the school, it would be helpful to seek further advice or guidance regarding the specific requirements of your institution if this isn't already offered. This could include:

• Asking for specific policies – as an example, those relating to behaviour for learning and safeguarding might be particularly helpful at this point.

• Access to relevant departmental schemes of learning or resources, particularly those relating to the Autumn term.

• A map of the school so that you can locate your teaching rooms in advance.

• A copy of the staff handbook or similar so that you can familiarise yourself with protocols.

Starting the academic year – your essential checklist

Towards the end of the summer holiday can be a good time to start your preparations for the Autumn term. From a practical perspective, ensure that you have any necessary equipment you might require. Please don't feel you need to spend the summer holiday completing work in readiness for Autumn. You need to enjoy the break and the chance it offers to fully unwind and relax. Furthermore, particularly if you are starting new at a school, you might find in September that any work you did in the holiday was misplaced as perhaps a scheme of learning has been changed or a required resource has already been created. As a conscientious individual, you will be ready when the time arrives to start teaching. Your department will be able to advise and support you with your preparations when you meet in the new term. You are better placed starting in September refreshed and full of energy than tired from a summer of work.

If you don't want to switch off completely, then an enjoyable preparation can involve exploring advice, stories or research through educational podcasts. There are a wealth of options available and they can be enjoyed as and when you feel like engaging with pedagogy. A quick internet search will give you an insight into the many podcasts that are available – have a browse to find the ones that interest you most. A starting point might be The Learning Scientists website – they have interesting, accessible videos and podcasts on cognitive science and education.

You may also want to consider becoming a member of the Chartered College of Teaching, which is a professional body for teachers that has a dedicated membership for ECTs and provides access to a range of additional materials.

Use the space on the next page to create your essential checklist. It is, of course, worth speaking to your department to find out what is already available as, depending on budgets and order deadlines, some of this can be provided.

Some possible items to consider are:

- Black/blue pens in addition to your colour pens for marking. You might want to consider having a small number of spare black/blue pens for those students who will invariably forget a pen and need to borrow one – a small kindness and one they will appreciate.
- Sticky notes – these can be very helpful for writing quick reminders on or as an easily transportable memo to be relayed to another member of staff or student.
- Notepad – this can be incredibly useful for keeping track of what needs to be done and when. See Autumn 2, Week 2 for further insight into utilising lists to promote efficiency and time management.
- Wireless presentation remote – these are available to purchase at little cost and are handy if you need to use PowerPoint. The USB plugs into the computer and the remote then allows you to move forward with the presentation without being tied to the keyboard.
- Thermal reusable mug – an essential if you want to have access to a hot tea or coffee during your well-deserved breaks and will save using disposable cups.

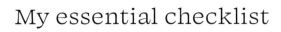

My essential checklist

- [ ]
- [ ]
- [ ]
- [ ]
- [ ]
- [ ]
- [ ]
- [ ]
- [ ]
- [ ]
- [ ]
- [ ]
- [ ]
- [ ]
- [ ]
- [ ]
- [ ]
- [ ]
- [ ]
- [ ]
- [ ]
- [ ]
- [ ]
- [ ]

That's it, you are ready to begin your Autumn term! Good luck – you've got this!

Autumn
term 1

Week 1
Researching your classes

New beginnings and the start of an academic year can bring mixed feelings for anyone returning to school (staff and students alike), but they can feel particularly pronounced for an ECT. Be reassured that this is perfectly normal. There might be slight trepidation as you wonder what lies ahead. What will my classes be like? What challenges might present themselves? However, there is also the excitement that the answers to these questions bring and by the end of a long summer holiday, a motivation to start in your new role. It is important to be particularly kind to yourself this week as emotions can feel pronounced with so many changes. Remember your list of support networks both within and beyond school and don't be afraid to reach out and share your feelings and experiences.

It is very unlikely that you will be teaching immediately at the start of term. Hopefully, this will provide you with some time to begin preparing for your classes. Be focused with prioritising your work here. This isn't the moment to spend hours creating a new display. Whilst first lessons invariably involve a certain amount of administration as you distribute books, etc., it is also an invaluable opportunity to start on the best possible footing with the students you will be teaching. Therefore, ensure that you have taken the time to do your research so that you have an insight into your classes and how this may assist with planning. For example, an awareness of students who are disadvantaged or who might have specific requirements such as disabilities or special educational needs. Are there any vulnerable individuals that you need to be mindful of? Have you considered reading ages or prior attainment indicators?

With a view to this and behaviour management, you should also think about establishing the classroom as your learning domain and seating plans are essential here for every class. They don't have to be perfect – indeed, until you meet your students, it can be difficult to get them completely right and there may be movement. The key is having a seating plan for each class. It frames the classroom as your space and helps to ensure that any relevant needs can be met.

Reflections

Research your classes using the prompts on the previous page to guide you. Reflect on how this information can help with adapting your planning and teaching to create an inclusive learning experience. Then take the time to create seating plans for each of your classes, drawing on your research of the students as appropriate.

Choose one class and, following your first lesson, reflect on the seating plan you created. What worked well? Where might you want to make edits and why? Is there any further information you might benefit from with regards to individuals in the class? Where could it be accessed from (either online, such as a central database, or from another professional, such as tutor, Head of Year or SENDCO)?

Consider the weekend ahead. What three treats can you give yourself after your first week at work? It could be reading in bed for an hour on Sunday morning, meeting friends for a drink, or going for that long walk you've craved all week. Ensure you stick to it. You've totally earned it and self-care is an absolute priority in demanding work such as teaching.

1.

2.

3.

Favourite
student quote

"

"

Highlight
of the week

41

Week 2
Meeting your classes

Week 2 is likely to be your first full week of lessons and unless your school operates on a two-week timetable, you will be meeting all your students. Clarifying expectations is essential this week. Frame these around core values so that you are creating a classroom culture rooted in shared key principles. For example, you might want to emphasise the need for respect and that this means ensuring hands are raised before questions are answered. In doing so, you are setting a positive tone with a clear rationale for establishing staff and student relationships that are conducive to learning. Indeed, transparency of boundaries is fundamental for a learning environment to help students feel safe as it makes it clear that you are in control. Communicating these boundaries to your class ensures that steps taken to maintain these expectations will be both fair and reasonable.

Never underestimate how far you can dictate the tone of the lesson so ensure that you model your own expectations. Always try to be ready at the door to welcome your students and don't be afraid to show enthusiasm and passion for your subject. Being positive about your students and the learning which will take place is not to the detriment of classroom control.

Finally, try not to jump to any judgements about students, even more so in this first full week of teaching, and always try to scrutinise the reason behind any more challenging behaviour. For example, if a student who had been listening well starts to become unfocused during a set task, it is possible that they simply do not understand what they are required to do. A clearly repeated explanation may be all that is necessary to help them engage and it might be a chance to consider if further scaffolding or explanatory support is required in future planning.

Notes

Reflections

At the start of at least one of your lessons this week, ensure that you are at the door to welcome students. How do they respond? Consider in what ways it helped 'set the tone' for a positive lesson start.

It is important to celebrate your successes after your first week. It is very easy for us to move past this to consider what could have been better, but the successes are just as important and deserve your time. You can build on them in the same way you can build on things that didn't go quite so well. Write down something you are pleased with from this first week, however small – it could be an area of learning, a conversation with a student or member of staff, a resource you created or a wellbeing strategy you have managed to maintain.

1, 7 TS Part 8: Personal and professional conduct

Favourite student quote

"

"

Highlight of the week

43

Think piece 1
Expectations

Having high expectations is a central feature of quality classroom practice. The *Great Teaching Toolkit Evidence Review* (Coe et al., 2020) presents four key 'priorities' for teacher efficacy: 'Understanding the content', 'creating a supportive environment', 'maximising opportunity to learn' and 'activating hard thinking'. Arguably, integral to all of these is having a high-expectation approach to both yourself as a professional and to the learning by students within your classroom.

Be careful not to equate high expectations to fast-paced content delivery or pitching material at a difficult level – this can be counter-productive. Indeed, where you are trying to engage students with more complicated ideas, recognise that there are stages to a deeper understanding (Willingham, 2009, p. 79). This means using your expertise as a practitioner to sequence the stages of learning appropriately to help transition students from novice to expert. You can explore this further in Think piece 4 (page 68). Planning and teaching in a way that allows students to access the content will still enable you to embed challenge whilst also ensuring that expectations are realistic. For example, now that all students can be involved in your lesson, there is no opportunity to 'opt out' with an 'I don't know' response (Lemov et al., 2016, p. 123).

In terms of behaviour, Dix highlights the necessity of being explicit with students on what your expectations are; you can't expect that they will just 'know' (2017, p. 22). He recommends incorporating three key routines into the expectations you communicate to students – warning that more than three and students will struggle to remember them all. Examples might include ensuring all students are silent and making eye contact before you start speaking (2017, pp. 77, 80). Then enact what he terms 'deliberate botherdness' (2017, p. 37), namely the regular, daily actions of staff towards students which show that they care by establishing positive expectations and recognising those who meet them (2017, p. 39). This might include acknowledging those students who look to go well beyond what is asked, or greeting students at the classroom door (2017, pp. 15, 42). It shouldn't involve celebrating those who meet basic expectations briefly, although it is still important that these individuals know that with the right choices they have the opportunity, like others, to receive recognition (2017, p. 44).

Follow the reward systems your school has in place here but remember that you are at the centre of setting, clarifying and delivering on expectations. If you expect respect in the classroom, then ensure that you model this. At the same time, always show students that you care and want the best for them.

Reflections

Past planning

Reflect on what your classroom expectations are with regards to learning and behaviour. How would you summarise them? How have you communicated these expectations to students and how successfully have they been met? What amendments might you want to make following the Think piece on the previous page?

Preparation

Observe a member of staff who has strong practice in this area and then use this to inform the next activity.

Look ahead to a lesson you have planned. How have you sequenced the learning within the lesson to enable appropriate challenge so that all can participate? Consider any amendments you might want to make accordingly.

Following Dix's guidance, which three routines might you want to set as basic expectations in your classroom and why? What steps can you take to communicate and embed these with your classes?

Follow-up

Return here to evaluate your amendments to the planning and establishment of routines. What next steps could you take to continue to maintain a high-expectation approach in the classroom? Remember, this is more inclusive than simply behaviour.

1, 3, 4, 7
TS

Week 3
Support networks and socials

Building a support network in school is crucial for any professional, perhaps even more so for an ECT. As a new member of staff, this first month is a vital opportunity to get to know your colleagues. Ensure that you are protecting your break and lunchtime. During a full day of teaching there may inevitably be some small tasks which need completing at these points, but it is also essential that you have some time for yourself. You don't want to create a habit now of working through these times. Instead, prioritise your break and lunchtime as an opportunity to speak to and get to know other members of staff, going to spaces such as the staffroom or similar if you have one. It is also important to attend social opportunities where they are presented.

Your fellow school ECTs are another essential support group to build relationships with. Therefore, continue to maintain lines of communication beyond your meetings and maximise the help you can provide each other by listening to successes or concerns and helping to talk through possible resolutions. However, equally advisable is to avoid any comparative or competitive talk regarding your experiences – this is unhealthy and only serves to increase anxieties rather than promote healthy relationships. If you work in a school with very few other ECTs, speak to your induction tutor about the possibility of meeting with ECTs from other schools within the area.

Notes

Reflections

Who would you list as your current support network in school? How has it helped you? How might you look to expand on this? Reflect on where there might be opportunities to speak to a new colleague, attend a social event or join an organisation. Have you had an opportunity to meet the other ECTs yet? If not, arrange a time to come together soon so that you can establish relationships as a group – this will be important as the year progresses.

Favourite student quote

"

"

Highlight of the week

Week 4
Working patterns

You are mid-way through the first half-term and now is the ideal time to take stock and scrutinise the working patterns you are starting to form. Are they healthy? Do they help with your own wellbeing? How many hours are you working a day? Refer back to your reflections and aims in the 'Your personal journey' section to guide your thinking.

In these first few weeks, you might have more time than anticipated, which can feel counter-intuitive. There may be no initial marking at this point, or you could be ahead with your lesson planning. Whatever the reason, when you can, continue to be encouraged to impose boundaries beyond the hours of a usual working day. Sometimes in teaching there can be a perceived pressure to work long hours, partly because it is a profession where this can be the case, but it doesn't mean you have to. Remember that most tasks can probably wait and if they can't, limit how far it intrudes on your plans – certainly don't make that late night a regular occurrence and avoid it if at all possible.

A kind colleague once told me how when she was working late marking, another teacher came and took the work off her and told her to go home. She refused to give it back, despite protestations, and assured her that the students would not even blink when they discovered that their work wasn't marked the next day. Not only was she right, but the sense of relief at also getting home that night and having some time to decompress was immeasurable. It is important to remind ourselves that we have to self-care to avoid burn out, which means you cannot work all of the time. Don't forget that if you are feeling overwhelmed, speak to your mentor, induction tutor or Head of Department.

Notes

Reflections

Look back at the wellbeing reflections that you completed at the beginning of the year. Are you on track with your aims? What adjustments could you make? Where feasible, try and leave slightly earlier than usual one day this week and use the time to complete an enjoyable activity or wellbeing-focused exercise.

Favourite student quote

"

"

Highlight of the week

Week 5
Managing relationships with students and staff

Teaching is an incredibly rewarding job but it can be emotionally draining and at this point in the term both you and your students are likely to be getting tired. However, it is important not to let this impact on your professionalism, particularly when there might be an interaction with a more challenging student. Remember, you are dealing with a child and part of your role is to help model the behaviour which is expected, so always try to manage your emotions. If you are genuinely feeling angry then try to find a way to pause so that you don't overreact – staying in control of yourself and the situation is essential.

Remember, if you issue a sanction, then the recommendation would be to follow through with it to show that you are consistent. However, if you've said something extreme in a moment of anger then you can end up compromising yourself. Try to take a deep breath and think carefully – what do I need to say and do? Who might I need to speak to for further advice here? Ideally, you need to ensure that you respond to a classroom incident as, in most circumstances, deferring to others will not help establish your authority.

You would still be encouraged to seek support and guidance when required and delaying action doesn't mean you are not seeking a resolution.

When experiencing frustrations with staff, it can be even harder – these are other professionals and should never be spoken to in the same way that you would speak to a child. Obviously, we hope that negative emotions are not elicited by colleagues. However, as with all places of work, it may well be that demands, personalities or ways of working are in conflict and education is no exception. If you have any concerns or worries, follow the appropriate systems in school to share this. For example, speaking to your induction tutor or mentor. If the difficulty doesn't impact on your work, then even if it does bother you, reflect on what you would hope someone can do about it to determine if further steps are required. If you need to vent, then do so with someone outside of your institution – not with colleagues who could be put in a compromised position.

Reflections

Consider a more challenging moment you have had with a student or member of staff so far. How did you respond? Reflecting on the guidance on the previous page, what went well? What might you do differently next time and why?

Favourite student quote

"

"

Highlight of the week

⭐

1, 7, 8
TS
Part 2: Personal and professional conduct

Think piece 2
Behaviour management

Behaviour management can understandably be an area of concern for ECTs. Having clarity of expectations is just one element of behaviour management, but how these are delivered and maintained is also essential.

Robert and Jana Marzanos' research (2003) argues that the defining feature of strong classroom management is positive teacher-student relationships, distinguished by several key features. These include being assertive as opposed to passive or aggressive, and showing command and clarity in the environment by using verbal and non-verbal signs to communicate where behaviour is and isn't acceptable with a consideration to both tone and body language (2003, pp. 6–9). When paired with taking a personal interest in students and a consistent, genuine focus on learning, behaviour can improve (2003, p. 9). As Bennett and Berry highlight, teachers shouldn't be afraid to show warmth. It shows every student that they are valued and that you want to seek to establish a positive professional relationship. This is distinct from being overfamiliar, which is not recommended. This means that you can ignore the oft-quoted guidance and absolutely smile before the half-term – to not do so at times would just appear strange (2017, p. 58).

Lemov, Hernandez and Kim offer some useful advice here with their term 'emotional constancy' (2016, p. 444), namely ensuring that you as the professional always remain calm and level in your manner thus offering security as students know that they can trust you are in control (2016, pp. 444–445). Remember to separate the behaviour from the individual (Bennett & Berry, 2017, p. 53). In doing so, you are not only a role model of the behaviour you expect but you avoid a student believing that there is anything personal being challenged. This also means avoiding large-scale classroom confrontation. Dix recommends a maximum of 30 seconds when engaging with a student regarding their poor classroom behaviour (2017, p. 92). Within this dialogue, he advises that you stick to a script whereby you stay focused on the primary behaviour and use the language of choice, reminding the child that they have control of the behaviours they are exhibiting and can make this right (Dix, 2017, pp. 93 –94). It is important that you stay in charge and remain calm and assertive, so that your classroom remains a safe space where your actions are seen as fair (2017, p. 93). If it helps, don't be afraid to have your response prepared in advance, so that you feel more empowered when it needs to be used (2017, p. 99). It is also always important to consider how classroom behaviour might link with barriers to learning and how the removal of these may facilitate improved engagement.

Finally, it is worth noting that the statutory guidance for ECTs stipulates that schools have a responsibility not to present ECTs 'on a day-to-day basis, with discipline problems that are unreasonably demanding for the setting' (DfEb, 2021, p. 15). If you have concerns, speak to your induction tutor in the first instance.

Reflections

Past planning

Following the guidance on the previous page, what would you identify as your strengths of behaviour management? What would be your areas for development?

Preparation

Starting with your development point above, speak to your mentor about organising an observation of a member of staff who has a strong practice in behaviour management.

Consider a time when you found behaviour with an individual or class more challenging. Is there a new script you might have written using Dix's guidance? Draft this below.

Follow-up

Return here to record what you learnt from your observation noted above and how it might inform your own classroom management. Consider assertiveness, command, clarity, verbal and non-verbal signs, tone and body language.

Week 6
Safeguarding

Safeguarding is a fundamental element of the educational remit and teachers can often be at the forefront of this; indeed, Part 2 of the Teachers' Standards explicitly references that teachers must have 'regard for the need to safeguard pupils' wellbeing, in accordance with statutory provisions' (DfE, 2021a, p. 14). You will have received in-house training and guidance on this and should have read Part 1 of the Department for Education's *Keeping children safe in education* (2021c).

However, as a new teacher, the reality of then experiencing a disclosure or a more challenging scenario can be emotionally demanding both during and after the event and you might find that you take home with you worries or feelings that are harder to process.

This is completely understandable – indeed, it simply shows how much you care – but it is important to share this with an appropriate individual so that you are supported.

Equally, you need to safeguard yourself, so remember to maintain your boundaries with students. This doesn't mean that you can't be friendly, but you do need to maintain your professionalism by following both the Teachers' Standards and your school's guidance. It is also worth reviewing your privacy settings on social media platforms to ensure that these are secure.

Key in all safeguarding areas is to keep an open mind to all possible occurrences and don't hesitate to seek help or advice if you have any concerns or queries (DfE, 2021c, p. 17).

Notes

Reflections

If you are unclear about any part of a school and teachers' legal responsibilities with safeguarding, revisit *Keeping children safe in education Part 1* (DfE, 2021c), which is available online. If you are confused about in-school processes, do seek immediate clarification with your designated safeguarding lead or similar.

    Now consider who might be an appropriate individual to speak to in school if you found yourself emotionally upset by a disclosure or scenario. Add these names to your support network list if they are not already on there.

    Finally, draw on your training to write down three key steps you can take to keep both yourself and children safe.

1.

2.

3.

Favourite student quote

"

"

Highlight of the week

TS
1, 8
Part 2: Personal and professional conduct

Week 7
Half-termly reflections (1)

Firstly, huge congratulations on making it to the end of the first half-term as an ECT. The start of an academic year requires a lot of energy, with getting to know classes and learning the many demands of a job within a new school. What have you got planned for the holiday? Ideally, try to take a break from work for the entire week – you will feel significantly more rested as a result. If you feel that it isn't possible, then compress what is required down to the absolute essentials and limit the time you assign to these tasks. Do not work every day or you won't feel like you've had a break – a week goes quickly! Where there is work to complete, really scrutinise whether a) it has to be done over the break and b) whether you would be more efficient and do a better job if you did it during term time.

Reflections

You should celebrate your achievements at the completion of this first half-term. Is there a school social event or similar that you could attend? If there isn't, could you and the other ECTs organise something together? If there are commitments outside of school time, it could be as simple as coming together at a lunchtime and sharing cake! Note down your ideas here.

_____

_____

The half-term week is time for some much-needed self-care. List three treats you are going to give yourself this half-term holiday and ensure that you stick to these regardless of other commitments – you have absolutely earned them!

1. _____

_____

2. _____

_____

3. _____

Don't forget that the only way you can continue to work hard in the education sector is if you take a decent rest now. Whilst it is a cliché, the often-quoted analogy holds – the reason you put your own oxygen mask on first is so that you are then better able to help others. Taking rest for yourself is the same. It will help you to manage the demands of school on your return and therefore don't for a minute feel bad about taking a break – it is what your holidays are for!

Favourite student quote

❝

❞

Highlight of the week

Reflect on this half-term with a focus on teaching and learning, professional development and wellbeing. What has gone well? Has it developed as you thought? What might you want to do differently next half-term?

• **Teaching and learning**

• **Professional development**

• **Wellbeing**

8
TS

57

Autumn
term 2

Week 1
Reflecting on your
professional development (1)

Welcome back to school! Hopefully you felt excited at the prospect of your return and ready for what it holds after a restful break. If this isn't the case, spend some time trying to identify why you might feel trepidation. Perhaps there are personal circumstances which meant you didn't quite get the rest you needed. Alternatively, it might be that there are anxieties about a class or topic that you are teaching. Please remember that whatever the reason, this is nothing to be embarrassed about. Indeed, recognising your concerns is a healthy sign that you are constantly reflecting on your practice. Be encouraged to share your worries with your mentor at your next meeting. Even if it is not school related, if you feel comfortable doing so, it is worth making them aware so that they can support you accordingly.

Either way, ensure that you spend some time with your tutor/mentor this week reflecting on the previous half-term. Your reflections from Autumn 1, Week 7 would work well as a starting point. You should also use this as an opportunity to return to your appraisal targets in preparation for your first professional progress review. How are you moving forward with these? What additional guidance or support might you still benefit from?

These dialogues are essential for embedding habits of reflective practice. Remember, the Teachers' Standards explicitly references this under Section 8 – 'Fulfil wider professional responsibilities' (DfE, 2021a, p. 13) and the ECF gives example of such practice including the feedback received from lesson observations, engaging in research and having the opportunity to collaborate with colleagues (DfE, 2019a, p. 24). Your engagement with the reflection activities in this journal so far will have already helped with your compilation of evidence in preparation for your review.

Notes

Reflections

Summarise the notes from your tutor/mentor meeting this week. What strengths from the first half-term did you identify together? How far have you progressed with your appraisal targets? Looking ahead, what support or next steps have you discussed as being helpful to aid continued progress? List these below.

Ensure that you have updated your Teachers' Standards table with notes of any additional relevant evidence you have collated.

TS 8

Favourite student quote

"

"

Highlight of the week

61

Think piece 3
Scaffolding

The term 'scaffolding' is frequently used in educational circles. It is understood to have been coined by Wood, Bruner and Ross (1976, p. 90) in their research into the tutorial process and how this assisted younger children as they learned. The educator allows an individual to move into what Vygotsky terms a 'Zone of Proximal Development' (1978, p. 85); namely to complete a task which they couldn't undertake without assistance. Then as students 'master' and 'internalise' the skills (1978, p. 88), the support can be reduced accordingly.

Rosenshine's 'Principles of instruction' article (2010) posits that scaffolding, specifically reducing the amount of information presented at one time and staggering how this is communicated with students, ensures that individuals can access the learning to avoid being overwhelmed. This includes the educator making use of modelling and worked examples to aid understanding. It means that gradually, through practice, teacher support can be reduced accordingly as students learn and internalise, returning to the previous prompts supplied for additional guidance when required (2010, pp. 10, 14–15). He terms this process 'cognitive apprenticeship' as students are gradually equipped with the necessary learning tools to complete tasks independently (2010, p. 22). It is worth noting that the *Great Teaching Toolkit Evidence Review* flags that Rosenshine's principles are best understood as theory drawn from a background of research (Coe et al., 2020, p. 46).

Examples of effective scaffolds could include checklists for self-evaluation; clarity in the stages of a task completion; poor model examples which require correction or conversely high-quality work for comparison (Rosenshine, 2010, p. 23). Sherrington (2019) is helpful at providing additional clarity here. Models could involve subject-specific examples or diagrams, rooting what might appear obscure to students in more concrete language; a teacher talking through a specific thought process as an example for the class; and the use of writing frames and exemplar answers (2019, pp. 18–23).

Remember, scaffolding can apply to all areas of educational practice including oracy, teacher written feedback, and questions or tasks including peer or self-assessment.

Reflections

Past planning

Reflect on how you have already made use of scaffolding in lessons to assist with learning. Which strategies or techniques have you deployed that you have found to be particularly successful?

Preparation

Consider which of the recommendations on the previous page you might want to make more use of more in lessons and think about where you might benefit from additional support with subject-specific examples, e.g. shared planning or observation of a colleague. Give examples of the steps you took to improve your understanding of scaffolding and how you deployed your chosen strategy/strategies.

Follow-up

Evaluate how effectively you felt these strategies worked, e.g. were students gradually able to internalise knowledge or skills with reduced teacher input? How could you measure this? How could you continue to promote this classroom practice?

Week 2
Strategies for managing workload

One of the more challenging elements of teaching is balancing the array of tasks which needs completing, often with different deadlines. Here, experience can be helpful for knowing which jobs to prioritise hence why it can feel more demanding as an ECT.

A useful technique is to divide activities into lists according to the time it is anticipated that each one will require. For example, list A could be activities that can be completed within a single planning, preparation and assessment (PPA) slot, e.g. checking, organising and responding to emails. List B might be tasks you allocate if you have a double PPA slot, e.g. reviewing and tailoring a lesson and resources as part of your planning for a class. List C might be if you need more time than one or two PPAs would allow and therefore it becomes a before or after-school task, e.g. reading a reflective piece of educational literature.

Once you have created your lists, plan your work over a week based on the time available in line with the tasks which need completing. This allows you to be more efficient and focused, and it can reduce the anxiety which a long list of 'to dos' can elicit. Of course, it isn't always possible to protect your time or to determine accurately how long an activity will take, despite our best intentions. Therefore, do allow for some flexibility, it is a system which can be adjusted accordingly.

Notes

Reflections

When planning for next week, map out your tasks into A, B and C lists based on the time they take and then plan them in relation to your availability in a working week. Try and follow this accordingly. At the end of the week, review how long the activities took. Was it as you had expected? How successful did you find this method for making efficient use of your time?

Favourite student quote

"

"

Highlight of the week

Week 3
Collaborative departmental planning

In July 2018, the Department for Education published a document on 'Ways to reduce workload in schools' (updated March 2019). It brought together a series of findings from working groups that sought to consider how teacher wellbeing could be improved by reducing workload across a variety of areas.

One element evaluated was the time spent curriculum planning (DfE, 2019b, p. 6). This is particularly pertinent for an ECT where, by virtue of delivering material for the first time, this can be a significant element of your job. The report gave several recommendations for helping this practice to become more sustainable. Firstly, look to share resources with colleagues where possible (DfE, 2019b, p. 6). Your department is likely to have a wealth of material already which could be pooled and save you creating resources from scratch. You can then focus

Reflections

Reflect on how much time, on average, you are spending planning across a week. How many hours have you spent on planning in the last week? Do you find the quantity of time reasonable or unmanageable? How is it impacting on work/life boundaries? For example, if you are planning every evening after a long day at school then this is not sustainable or healthy. Instead, speak to your mentor or Head of Department about the possibility of sharing resources to help reduce your workload.

Favourite student quote

"

on tailoring this material to the
needs of your students. Alternatively,
ask your Head of Department to
divide up the content which is to
be planned so that you can work
with a more experienced colleague
(DfE, 2019b, p. 6). The Think
piece on page 68 highlights how
professionally enriching shared
planning can be with the added
benefit of protecting valuable time.

"

Highlight of the week

★

★

Consider how you are using your PPA time and look to organise shared planning
with a more experienced colleague. Write down your reflections and action plan,
then return to update it with the outcomes. If you can, total up the amount of time
you spent or saved by following these revised systems – hopefully it has reduced
without impacting on quality.

3, 4
TS

Think piece 4
Subject and curriculum knowledge

Allison and Tharby argue that improved student performance is rooted in those teachers who not only have the strongest understanding of their curriculum areas but are then able to effectively translate this into the classroom (2015, p. 5). This is supported by the findings of the *Great Teaching Toolkit Evidence Review*, which states: 'Great teachers understand the content they are teaching and how it is learnt'. They explain that 'this means teachers should have deep and fluent knowledge and flexible understanding of the content they are teaching... including its inherent dependencies. They should have an explicit repertoire of well-crafted explanations, examples and tasks for each topic they teach' (Coe et al., 2020, p. 17).

One essential element to this is that teachers can effectively identify, plan and teach what key knowledge students need to know and then assess accordingly (Wiliam & Christodoulou, 2017, p. 35). Ruth Ashbee's distinction between 'substantive' and 'disciplinary' knowledge might be helpful here (2021, p. 32). The former is the key content that needs to be conveyed to students, whilst the latter is how that knowledge was constructed or developed within the specific academic discipline. The challenge for the teacher is to plan and deliver on both these key elements, relevant to the specific educational stage (2021, p. 32). For example, what is 'core' knowledge for one year group – the essential points of a subject – will provide the required background for 'hinterland' knowledge at a later point – the additional detail required to give a fuller body to the core (2021, p. 38).

ECTs will be guided on what these key elements are by their Head of Department and need to use this information to compare learning schemes and draw links between them in preparation for their teaching. It is also recommended to plan for a unit rather than a lesson. Fletcher-Wood argues that this allows for a more comprehensive pedagogical overview. Key knowledge can be covered in a meaningful sequence so that more complex learning is built on foundational knowledge, seeking to address possible misconceptions which might arise, and building in opportunities for retrieval practice and schematic connections (2018, pp. 20–28).

This sequencing can be particularly challenging for an ECT, especially when it involves material which is previously unexplored or learnt. Seek to grow and develop your own professional development and use this in turn to pitch and plan your lesson material. Working with more experienced colleagues in the department will be a starting point for these conversations including shared planning and scheduled observations.

Reflections

Past planning

Consider a unit of learning that you have already planned. What helped guide you in terms of the key knowledge to include? How far did you feel confident in teaching this material and what steps did you take to improve your expertise?

Preparation

Look ahead to a unit of learning that you need to plan. Which colleague/s could you meet with to seek additional guidance or support in planning for possible misconceptions and opportunities for retrieval practice and schematic connections? Also, use this as an opportunity to learn about effective scaffolding, modelling and explanatory strategies that they would recommend from their experience. If it helps you, use this to script classroom teaching that you would like to trial.

Follow-up

Once you have taught your unit of learning, return here to evaluate it. With reflection, how well prepared was your planning in covering the guidance on the previous page? What further edits or improvements might you make when planning your next unit of learning? Are there any additional steps you might take in looking for support?

3, 4

TS

Week 4
Communicating with parents, carers and guardians

The school community is made up of multiple agencies and integral to this is the role of parents, carers and guardians, an essential element in the professional relationship between schools and students. This means, as far as possible, involving parents, carers and guardians in any relevant dialogue so that they are aware of potential concerns or successes. Your school will have a system for maintaining these lines of contact with a view to sanctions and rewards and it is important that you follow these. Within this, it is advisable not to see a phone call home as a last resort. Rather, recognise the value of positive phone calls or messages. The chance for a student's parent, carer or guardian to hear something that their son/daughter is doing well is always welcomed and a lovely routine for you to instigate.

Where there are concerns, a regular dialogue with home which is centred on learning can help to reduce escalation. A parent, carer or guardian might understandably feel surprised to hear of any issues for the first time in line with a more serious sanction, unless, of course, a student's chosen behaviour demands it. If you can, take the time to involve home, which will serve to reinforce your classroom expectations. Celebrating those students who are getting it right is just as central to this and will improve your relationships with them by showing how invested you are in their development. Equally, it is important not to create additional workload for yourself so use the systems your school has available to aid the process here. For example, send an email to home or attend parent, carer and guardian consultation evenings.

As always, where there are concerns or a more difficult conversation is required, involve your mentor and/or Head of Department so that you are supported in following the appropriate steps, and always focus on the behaviour not the individual. It is worth noting that communicating 'effectively with parents' (DfE, 2021a, p. 13) is a requirement for Teachers' Standards 8 so the reflections you make on the next page are evidence you can use towards this.

Reflections

Take some time this week to have at least one positive communication with home for a student. How did the parent, carer or guardian respond? How did the student respond? Reflect on how regularly you might seek to do this and why.

TS 1, 7, 8

Favourite student quote

"

"

Highlight of the week

⭐

71

Think piece 5
Feedback

When utilised effectively by practitioners, feedback is integral for facilitating progress. The Education Endowment Foundation (EEF) is a charity who use evidence drawn from research to create a 'Teaching and Learning toolkit' webpage that rates the impact of several educational approaches (2021). It also reviewed the ECF (DfE, 2019a, p. 2) and their toolkit provides a helpful accompaniment to a range of areas in the framework.

The EEF defines feedback as 'information given to the learner about the learner's performance relative to learning goals or outcomes. It should aim to (and be capable of producing) improvement in students' learning' (EEF, 2021). Wiliam and Christodoulou (2017) helpfully highlight that the strength of the feedback a teacher can provide is dictated by the task which is set. It is essential that your planning allows for students to illustrate their understanding so that you can then meaningfully diagnose and respond to this (2017, p. 33). The nature of the teacher's response needs to be instructive and clear so that a student can engage with what is being asked (2017, p. 29). Wiliam summarises this guidance as 'feedback should cause thinking' (2018, p. 142). One suggestion here includes the use of questions which students have to respond to (2018, p. 144). Alternatively, whole-class guidance can be offered on where improvements are required. Students then have to utilise this instruction to scrutinise their own work for specific development points to action (2018, p. 145).

It is important to remember the multiple forms feedback can take, incorporating a range of strategies such as those set out by Allison and Tharby. These include:

- the verbal feedback you can provide within a lesson in response to students' answers or work, then getting the individual to repeat this or action it so that you can ensure they understand

- peer assessment supported by teacher-created success criteria to provide structure and consistency

- coding as opposed to repeated comments – the students match the symbol with shared improvement questions that they can copy and respond to

- a 'five-minute flick' where a sample of student work is checked and used as an analysis for the whole-class explanatory feedback during the next lesson (2015, pp. 179–195).

This modelling then leads to meaningful self-assessment by the students (2015, p. 197). Allison and Tharby end with the sound advice that if your diagnostic assessment indicates a benefit in reteaching, then don't hesitate to do so, with the knowledge that this is also a form of responsive feedback (2015, pp. 199–200).

Reflections

Past planning

Reflect on how you have utilised feedback so far within your practice. Which techniques have you found to be effective and why? Remember to consider how much students had to engage with the feedback and whether you observed impact.

Preparation

Observe a member of staff who has strong practice in this area. Then choose a feedback strategy from the previous page to trial. Explain how you designed its use and engaged students with the task. Give examples of how you deployed the strategy/strategies in the classroom and how this was informed by your observation.

Follow-up

Evaluate how effectively students engaged with the feedback and whether you observed improvement in their learning as a result. How will you now use this reflection to inform future practice? Is there an alternative technique you would look to try? How could you continue to promote this classroom practice?

2, 4, 6
TS

Week 5
Making marking meaningful

The 'Ways to reduce workload in schools' report referenced in Autumn 2, Week 3 recognised the impact feedback and marking can have on a teacher's workload (DfE, 2019b, p. 5). As you have read in Think piece 5 (Feedback), this is an area where research has been paramount at moving the pedagogy forward. Marking is not the only form feedback can take and when it is required, in terms of impact on student learning and facilitating progress, it is now about quality over quantity. The report produced by the independent teacher workload review group in 2016 suggested that the principles of effective marking could be structured around 3 Ms:

- **Meaningful** – Be clear about the purpose of the feedback and how it promotes progress.
- **Manageable** – What is required from staff should be reasonable and proportionate to the task.
- **Motivating** – In terms of students engaging and moving forward, feedback should be motivating (DfE, 2016, pp. 8, 10).

This means that you should no longer be having to regularly work through a set of books to provide extensive written feedback. Here, the 'Ways to reduce workload in schools' report has several helpful recommendations for alternative strategies. For example, if you do need to look at a piece of work completed by the whole class, be clear about the rationale for your selection. Then consider if you could you use one of the alternative feedback strategies, such as a shared written code or whole-class guidance, based on a sample of books. When questions are well-designed, tools such as Kahoot or Google Forms can also be effective as self-marking platforms to gauge whole-class understanding (DfE, 2019b, p. 5).

Notes

Reflections

Reflect on how much time you are spending on marking on average across a week. Total up the time from the past week. Do you find the quantity of time reasonable or unmanageable? How is it impacting on work/life boundaries? Does it seem that quantity is being prioritised over quality? If so, what could change?

Select one of the alternative strategies which are suggested for marking and evaluate how effective you found it. Did you gain a sense of students' understanding of their learning? Were you able to use this diagnosis to provide further feedback or to plan according to students' needs? Write down your reflections and then update them with the outcomes. If you can, total up the new quantity of time you spend or save following a revised system – hopefully it has reduced without impacting on quality.

2, 6
TS

Favourite student quote

"

"

Highlight of the week

Week 6
Participating in pastoral provision

The pastoral provision which schools offer alongside the curriculum is a fundamental part of an educational institution's role and teachers are often at the forefront of this. It is therefore likely that you are already involved in this in some way, perhaps as a tutor to students. If you are not, speak to your mentor about how you can participate in this system.

Getting to know and support the young people who you work with from a different perspective is an incredibly enriching experience. This can range from delivering a tutor-time activity to having a conversation with a student about what they did at the weekend. It gives you the chance to broaden your knowledge of who they are as individuals and to understand

Reflections

Note down what pastoral support you have been involved with so far and reflect on your experiences. What have you found enriching about this and why? Then consider if there is an area which particularly interests you that you would like to know more about. What steps could you take to facilitate this? Consider speaking to a Head of Year or similar individual to find out more about the spectrum of pastoral provision which is available in your school.

further what challenges they might face on several different levels both within and beyond school. In turn, the support you can offer allows you to develop your impact beyond the classroom as well as within it. You will often find that this further motivates you with your work as it can give a renewed focus to how you can help students, schools being uniquely placed in how they can support the young people in their care.

Favourite student quote

"

"

Highlight of the week

★

★

It would also be advisable to observe, or even shadow, strong pastoral practitioners. Record your reflections here. How have they helped further inform your understanding of the features of an outstanding pastoral programme?

8
TS

Week 7
Revisiting appraisal targets (1)

Congratulations – you have completed the Autumn term as an ECT! This is a fantastic achievement. For now, it is time to take a much-deserved break over the holiday. Don't forget to set up your out-of-office response on emails and try to earmark some time to rest. There is no expectation to look at your inbox until the new term starts.

Thinking about planning or marking? Look back at your reflections from Autumn 2, Weeks 3 and 5 to remind yourself of the strategies you can deploy for these to promote efficiency and maintain quality in the new term. Don't spend any more time on this over the holiday – you need a break, the Autumn term is particularly long.

You will have had your professional progress review with your mentor this term, which can form the basis of your reflections. At the beginning of this year (Autumn 1, Week 3) we discussed the importance of building companionship with colleagues within the school to ensure that you have a support network, essential in any role but particularly within the demands of teaching. Fellow ECTs will be an integral part of this experience, as you share your journey together through these first stages of the profession. Sometimes you may find yourself making comparisons with your peers, particularly following a progress review. Whilst looking to learn from others is a strength, don't see these reviews as a chance to compare or consider where you might have inadequacies. Instead see them as opportunities to improve, something that as teachers we should always be striving to do.

Notes

Reflections

Use this week's reflections to celebrate the professional growth you have made so far. Return to your reflections from the first week of the school year as you initially met your classes and consider the relationships you have built and how much the young people in your care will have already learnt. Think about the pastoral provision you have already been able to offer. Look at your weekly student quotes and highlights to remind yourself of the many positive experiences you have had. What have been the best parts of your first term as an ECT?

Now consider your developmental targets from the targets table on page 14. Use your notes from your professional progress review to chart your development and to look forward to where you would still like to grow. Consider what additional support or resources may assist with this. The Think pieces you have completed in this journal may be a helpful starting point for framing your reflections. Ensure your Teachers' Standards evidence table is updated and use this to help track and guide your continued progress.

Favourite
student quote

"

"

Highlight
of the week

Spring
term 1

Week 1
Re-establishing your expectations

Hopefully you have enjoyed a restful Christmas break and are returning to work feeling rejuvenated and ready for the new term. This first week back is an excellent opportunity to return to your wellbeing aims from the beginning of the last term as the focus of your reflections.

With regards to your classes, ensure that you begin positively after the break and re-establish your expectations. However last term ended does not need to define the start of this term. Hold no grudges against students who might have been more challenging. Instead, remember to welcome everyone at the door and continue to build positive, mutually respectful professional relationships. It can be as simple as a 'Welcome back, did you have a good break? How lovely to see you all' to make the students know that you want to be there teaching them.

Reflections

Look back at your wellbeing targets. How far have you been able to meet your self-care aims from the beginning of the first term? As always, don't be concerned or angry with yourself if you haven't fulfilled these in the way you hoped. Be kind in your reflections, recognising that completing a first term as an ECT is a huge achievement and that understandably there was a lot of work which came with it. Crucially, now is the time to consider what adjustments you need to make so that you don't compromise on your physical and mental health and can continue to meet or start meeting some of the aims you set out for yourself.

Favourite student quote

"

Notes

"

Highlight of the week

★

★

Now consider what steps you have taken after the Christmas holiday to consolidate your expectations and promote a positive classroom environment.

TS
1

Week 2
Extra/Supra-curricular provision

The extra and supra-curricular activities which schools make available to students are an integral part of the educational offering. The opportunity to become involved in these is often a highlight of the teaching profession as a role which is far more holistic than just classroom practice. During your first term, understandably it might have felt like this would be too much to take on as you established yourself. Now is an ideal time to investigate how you can participate in this offering with the Autumn term completed. Research whether there is a club or activity that interests you which you could get involved with, either within or beyond your department.

This is an excellent chance to develop professional relationships with students from a new perspective and to contribute to the fabric of

Reflections

Look at the clubs or activities offered within your school. Which particularly interest you? This week, try to approach the relevant member of staff leading on this to see if you can become involved in some way. Be honest about how much you can offer – remember, you do not want to add to your workload. However, also be realistic about what they might need from you – turning up once a term might not be of much assistance!

the school whilst simultaneously enriching both your own and others' experiences. It also presents another opportunity to expand your support network, by meeting new colleagues and cementing your place as part of the school.

It also worth noting that it would contribute as evidence towards Teachers' Standard 8 – 'fulfil wider professional responsibilities'. If you are feeling brave, you could even look to start your own offering, but be very mindful of your workload – you want to enhance your experiences, not become overwhelmed.

Favourite student quote

"

"

Highlight of the week

⭐

⭐

Write down the steps that you have taken to organise this and then return once you have attended to add what you enjoyed most about the activity you were able to engage with. How do you think it helped to make a positive contribution to the school community?

8
TS

Think piece 6
Responsive teaching

As educators, formative assessment is essential for ascertaining students' learning to inform planning and teaching. David Perkins speaks of 'fragile knowledge syndrome', the set of frequent issues students can present which are barriers to progress. This might include for example 'gaps' in understanding or 'confusion' on how learning should be applied and can often be the systematic experience of students in education (1992, p. 27).

Fletcher-Wood's concept of 'responsive teaching' provides a way of recognising these needs and being able to react accordingly (2018, p. 4). Drawing on the ideological basis of formative assessment and supported by cognitive science and research evidence, it involves finding meaningful strategies for checking students' understanding and then responding accordingly (2018, p. 9). This is particularly important given that students themselves are not always aware of what they do and don't know and if they are, some are unlikely to volunteer the information.

Fletcher-Wood gives an example of how an 'exit ticket' can be carefully designed to ensure that it covers the key knowledge points for the lesson, providing an insight into the varying learning responses, including gauging any misunderstandings (2018, p. 62). He flags the need to be hesitant of the claim that one can ascertain 'learning' at the end of a lesson, defined as 'a permanent change in behaviour or knowledge' and how this should not be understood to equate to 'performance' – 'a temporary fluctuation in behaviour or knowledge' (2018, p. 60). However, there is still a necessity to try to have a sense of students' knowledge or misunderstandings so that a teacher can then plan to respond accordingly in the next lesson (2018, p. 61).

Exit tickets can include open questions but also lend themselves to multiple-choice quizzes (MCQ). The latter also serve a use within a lesson to give whole-class feedback to a teacher by way of mini whiteboards or fingers (Fletcher-Wood, 2018, p. 85). It is essential to ensure that the MCQ are well designed so that there is plausibility in each of the possible answers available and to elicit any erroneous understandings (2018 p. 81). Fletcher-Wood terms these MCQ 'hinge questions' and states that they should be followed up by student justification of their answers. The teacher can then respond to any misconceptions in their lesson, withholding the correct answer so that students can learn what it is through the new exploration of the material (2018, pp. 80, 86, 89).

Reflections

Past planning

How have you made use of responsive teaching so far? Which strategies have you found to be more or less effective and why? Can you give a supporting example from your practice to illustrate your understanding?

Preparation

Observe a member of staff who has strong practice in this area. Using the guidance provided on the previous page, design a MCQ for use with a class as either an exit ticket or activity within a lesson. Explain how you planned the questions to ensure that the answers were plausible and would provide an insight into students' learning, including potential misconceptions. Explain how your planning was informed by your observation.

Follow-up

Evaluate what you learnt from your use of the MCQ. Was it effectively diagnostic? How did the answers help shape your planning and teaching so that you were responsive to your findings? What might you need to tweak for a future MCQ? How will you now use this reflection to inform future practice?

Week 3
Observations of other staff members

The guidance for the induction of ECTs stipulates that opportunities should be presented for the observation of other 'experienced teachers' either in your school or elsewhere (DfE, 2021b, p. 19). These observations are an opportunity to see quality teaching and learning in practice relating to areas of your professional development. The reflective guidance that appears at the end of each of this journal's Think pieces will help you undertake these regularly as an integral part of your ECT journey. Your mentor will also be best placed to direct you on what and who you should observe, in line with your own needs.

It is recommended that you have a clear focus prior to attending your observation and that you make notes of techniques and strong practice. Your school may provide a crib sheet for these observations but, if not, having your own notebook to keep records in works well. Where possible, arrange to have a follow-up discussion with the member of staff you observed – this can be a great chance for you to ask questions or explore further the excellent practice you saw. Remember, all teachers are invested in professional growth and are therefore unlikely to mind giving up time to help you.

Finally, ensure that you reflect on what you can learn and utilise from these observations and evaluate your own implementation in the classroom. Remember, it is not about comparisons, but rather part of your professional learning journey that allows you to be the best teacher you can be, whilst also remaining authentic to who you are as an individual.

Notes

Reflections

Consider an observation you have completed of another member of staff so far this year. Summarise your reflections on the process of the observation. Were you able to take notes? Could you have a follow-up discussion with the member of staff? Were you able to take away techniques or strategies for your own classroom practice and did you then evaluate how effectively these worked? How helpful did you find the experience and what steps might you take to improve the learning process next time?

8
TS

Favourite student quote

"

"

Highlight of the week

Week 4
Observations and feedback on your practice

An essential formative component of your induction process as an ECT will be the observations you receive of your lessons (DfE, 2021b, pp. 19–20). The statutory guidance stipulates that following these observations you must have the opportunity to meet with the observer and this verbal conversation should be accompanied with shared written records highlighting your next developmental areas (DfE, 2021b, p. 21).

As with all educational practitioners, you will likely have had some lessons which have worked better than others in terms of the learning facilitated. Be reassured that this is the case regardless of where you are in your teaching career. However, sometimes a series of development points might feel demoralising, particularly if you spent an extended time planning a lesson. The key here is resilience – see these observations as an opportunity to learn and grow your pedagogical

Reflections

Evaluate a lesson you have taught this week as if you had been the observer. What would you identify as the key strengths? What development points would you recommend? Make sure these are focused on learning using the ECF to guide you. How will these reflections help you with your future planning? Be mindful of your inner critic – ensure you challenge any negative criticism and instead focus on constructive advice.

Favourite student quote

66

....

....

....

99

Highlight of the week

skills. The feedback is designed to be constructive and is not an indictment of your practice. You will also find that adopting this attitude helps to cultivate a positive sense of self throughout your journey as a teacher as you continue to relish chances to develop your understanding of successful classroom practice.

4, 8

TS

Think piece 7
Mindsets

Educators can have a pivotal role in developing a student's mindset and when considering how self-belief can impact on learning, the work of Carol Dweck is central. She suggests that students can be helped in education by promoting what she terms a 'growth mindset' (2017, p. 91). This involves helping young people believe that they can improve, with the understanding that their learning ability is not already 'fixed' but rather that every individual has the capacity to develop and progress through opportunities, productive struggle and hard work (2017, p. 10). She flags that recognising process here is broader than effort (2017, p. 98). Students could be celebrated for the time they have spent completing a given activity, or equally seeking guidance when required, or for deploying a new approach to a task when stuck. The key is creating a classroom environment where students recognise that their teacher is invested in the learning development of every individual and that stereotypes or labels are seen as irrelevant. In this way, students and teacher share the mutual belief that they all have the 'potential to grow' (2017, p. 98) as part of a high-expectation approach.

To translate this into the classroom, try and create what Lemov et al. term a 'culture of error', namely a space where students see mistakes as an opportunity to learn (2016, p. 95). This means actively promoting the idea that it is healthy to get something wrong or to have a go at answering a question even when an individual is not sure (2016, p. 95). Furthermore, withhold confirming immediately the accuracy of a given response so that there are opportunities to explore multiple answers and the reasoning behind these.Be mindful here to manage your verbal and non-verbal cues in response to an answer which may 'tell' your view on the quality of the response (Lemov et al., 2016, p. 96).

Promoting a growth mindset amongst students arguably has benefits across the spectrum of education. For example, Allison and Tharby emphasise how students who recognise that they can academically improve are more likely to actively seek and collaborate in the feedback process (2015, p. 167). Teachers' Standards 4 stipulates that you 'promote a love of learning and children's intellectual curiosity' (DfE, 2021a, p. 11) and arguably integral to this is promoting the right classroom environment and thus mindset for students. It is worth noting that Dweck highlights the importance of holding the same mindset as teachers (2017, p. 93), namely recognising that professionally we should continually seek to grow and learn.

Reflections

Past planning

Reflect on how you might have already promoted a growth mindset in your classroom. Are there strategies you have deployed which you have found to be particularly successful? Consider your own development. How have you evidenced a growth mindset in your own practice?

Preparation

How could you further create a 'culture of error' in your lessons where all students believe they have the 'potential to grow'? Observe a member of staff who has strong practice in this area. Choose one of the techniques from the previous page and trial it over a series of lessons. Give examples of how you deployed the strategy/ strategies in the classroom and how this was informed by your observation.

Follow-up

Evaluate how effectively you felt this technique worked, e.g. did some of the quieter students participate who wouldn't have normally? How could you continue to promote this classroom environment? Consider how your evaluation process is evidence of your own growth mindset.

Week 5
Metacognition

The Classroom Practice section of the ECF references the need to 'explicitly' teach students 'metacognitive strategies' (DfE, 2019a, p. 15). The EEF clarify that metacognition is one strand of encouraging students to take a self-regulatory approach to their learning as part of teaching 'pupils to think about their own learning more explicitly'. It is rated as a high-impact approach, supported by a strong evidence base (2021). Their recommendation is that these should be domain-specific skills – namely, techniques relevant to the subject area you are teaching, such as evaluating how to plan an exam answer effectively in your curriculum. The EEF explains that your role as a professional is to guide students to learn these as you would key subject knowledge, e.g. teacher modelling – considering challenge and scaffolding – allowing for regular opportunities for individuals to monitor and evaluate their progress.

In doing so, pupils can gradually internalise these methods and gain metacognitive autonomy (EEF, 2021).

Indeed, sharing some of your classroom reflections with students can help you become a role model for metacognitive behaviour. Where time allows, take to mentally evaluating as many of your lessons as you can, which aren't being observed, so that you are embedding a habit of constantly reflecting and seeking to progress. Don't be afraid to then verbalise this to the students during a lesson, where appropriate. For example, 'I can see that we actually need to revisit our learning of this key concept first before we can complete this activity' or 'Can we recall from the last lesson what steps we could take to solve this problem?'. In doing so, you are also being a professional role model of metacognitive behaviour, focusing on progress and process, rather than attainment or completing a task tick list (EEF, 2021).

Notes

Reflections

With an experienced colleague in your department, discuss which metacognitive skills are recommended for you to teach students in your subject area. List them below. Can you explain how this shared planning process allowed you to embed explicit metacognitive teaching into your lesson sequences? What could be the benefit for students with their subject-specific learning? Remember, this isn't about creating more work but rather habituating professional practices which help to promote student progress.

Favourite
student quote

"

"

Highlight
of the week

1, 2, 3, 4
TS

Week 6
Half-termly reflections (2)

This is your last week of the first Spring term and, with March approaching, the end of winter is in sight. Think of the warmer, longer days with more sunlight, and summer not too far away now! As before, consider how you can spend your half-term to promote rest and recovery. By this point, you will hopefully have a clearer sense of what work is a priority and what can wait. Some staff find it beneficial for their wellbeing to 'get ahead' in the holidays as it reduces workload in the new half-term. If this is you, as discussed before, limit how much work this entails to a morning or two at most. Don't assign whole days to work – you'll only dread it. Remember how much more efficient you will be within the pressures of a working week once you are fully rested, so if it can wait... let it wait! For the same reason, if you plan to take the whole week off, absolutely do. There is a reason for regular holidays – both staff and students need them.

Reflections

Reflect on this half-term with a focus on teaching and learning, professional development and wellbeing. What has gone well? Has it developed as you thought? What might you want to do differently next half-term?

- **Teaching and learning**

- **Professional development**

- **Wellbeing**

Favourite student quote

"

"

Highlight of the week

★

★

Notes

The half-term week is a time for some much-needed self-care. List three treats you are going to give yourself this half-term holiday and ensure that you stick to these regardless of other commitments – you have absolutely earned them!

1.

2.

3.

8
TS

Spring
term 2

Week 1

Reflecting on your professional development (2)

You are now essentially halfway through your first academic year as a qualified teacher. You should feel incredibly proud of yourself! As always, the first week back provides an excellent chance to review working habits and consider where tweaks can be made to improve self-care. Your reflections from Spring 1, Week 6 would work well as a starting point. As far as possible, are you managing to keep your lunchtimes for speaking to colleagues and having a break from work? Have you continued to prioritise eating well across the working week to maximise energy levels? Now is a good time to look ahead to future holidays – it is never too early to start planning ahead for an activity in the Easter or Summer holiday.

Spend some time with your tutor/mentor this week reflecting on last half-term. You should also use this as an opportunity to return to your appraisal targets in preparation

Reflections

Summarise the notes from your tutor/mentor meeting this week. What strengths from last term did you identify together? How far have your progressed with your appraisal targets? Looking ahead, what support or next steps have you discussed as being helpful to aid continued progress? List them below. Make sure that you have updated your Teachers' Standards table with notes of any additional relevant evidence you have collated.

8
TS

for your second professional progress review. How are you moving forward with these? What additional guidance or support might you still benefit from? Hopefully you have been able to keep a track of your evidence collection in your Teachers' Standards table. Don't forget that this is in addition to your journal reflections, which are already charted on it. If you are still finding the amount of work is too much to manage across a week, share your weekly plans with your tutor/mentor from Autumn 2, Week 2 and consider where you could be spending less time and how.

Favourite student quote

"

"

Highlight of the week

★

Plan an event – whether a visit, trip, holiday, activity or hobby – for one of the future holidays. Detail what you have planned and visualise how you will feel during this time. Remind yourself of this when you are having a more challenging day at work.

Think piece 8
Retrieval practice

Developments with cognitive science research have helped inform the pedagogy of memory and learning. This can be seen in the descriptions of 'How Pupils Learn' in the ECF (DfE, 2019a, pp. 10–11). In his seminal text *Why Don't Students Like School?*, Willingham explains that our 'working memory' is our present consciousness and thus limited in capacity (2009, p. 11). Therefore, necessary to activating thinking in the classroom is to facilitate students pairing their 'working memory' with their 'long-term memory' as it is this which has the required facts and methods (2009, p. 13).

This has several implications for teaching, not least that having an awareness of what students already know in their long-term memory is integral to ensuring appropriate challenge. If you set a task that individuals don't have the necessary information for, then they will struggle to engage (Willingham, 2009, p. 15). Furthermore, where they have this prior learning available, it is essential to plan for opportunities to draw on it so that it can be applied to their new learning – this is known as retrieval practice. It can take the form of regular 'practice' and if it is utilised at frequent intervals across an academic year then the skills and knowledge required are more likely to stick (Willingham, 2009, p. 94).

Rosenshine explains that this 'chunking' helps students progress towards becoming experts. As their long-term memory stores, cements and connects the information, it creates space in their working memory for new learning (2010, p. 26). Didau clarifies how 'interleaving' – regularly revisiting a range of content over a period of time – can thus benefit the consolidation of prior and new knowledge (2019, p. 157). Wiliam and Christodoulou recommend 'regular testing' for students to retrieve prior learning (2017, pp. 34–35). This can be self-assessed to reduce staff workload, which has the added benefit of the 'hypercorrection effect' (2017, p. 35), namely that when marking themselves, students are more likely to remember the correct answer in lieu of their previously confident response.

Don't be concerned if you discover in your retrieval practice activity that students have forgotten what you have taught – this provides an opportunity to reteach the material. The research of Ebbinghaus suggests that individuals are then more open to relearning the material and gradually forget it less (Wiliam & Christodoulou, 2017, p. 56).

Reflections

Past planning

Reflect on how you have planned for retrieval practice in your sequences of learning. Consider how you acted responsively to the information it provided on learning retained by students in their long-term memory.

Preparation

Look to plan for regular testing of prior knowledge across a future sequence of learning. Ensure it is spaced, i.e. that there is time between it being taught and asking students to recall their learning. Where possible, interweave the topics that are required to be retrieved. Give examples of how you deployed this. Consider where you might benefit from additional support with subject-specific retrieval practice, e g. shared planning or observation of a colleague.

Follow-up

Evaluate how effectively students engaged with the retrieval activities. How did you diagnose and respond to the information you gained about students' learning? For example, did you subsequently revisit a curriculum area? Were students able to make synoptic links between old and new knowledge? How could you continue to promote this classroom practice?

Week 2
Managing anxieties

By nature of working in a secondary school and/or a Sixth Form college, much of the focus will be on the approaching exam season. This can cause additional anxiety for both staff and students. If you are teaching an exam year group, you may feel pressure in some form – perhaps because there is a certain amount of content you still need to cover, or more broadly because you are worried about what students might achieve. You might still have these concerns with other classes in other years.

Whatever the reason, firstly, feel encouraged to talk to your mentor about any anxieties so that they can reassure you and assist you with your concerns. Don't forget that you are an ECT who is entitled to support. Secondly, remember the importance of being a professional

Reflections

This week, focus on having some time around work to have a moment of calm. Reflect on what steps you can take if you need some time to relax. Headspace is a mindfulness tool which offers free access for educators and guidance on meditative breathing (https://www.headspace.com/educators). Alternatively, search 'BBC Headroom' for a range of soundscapes or music mixes designed to help you relax.

Favourite student quote

"

"

role model for students. If they can see that you are worried, then this is only going to exacerbate any concerns they have. Therefore, in the classroom demonstrate a calm, controlled manner and continue to cultivate your learning environment of high expectations to facilitate best outcomes for all. Take confidence in all the outstanding work you have done this year as demonstrated in this journal!

Highlight of the week

Which relaxation techniques have you tried that you have found to be successful? Note these below and return to them as required.

Week 3
Homework

Homework is something that you are likely setting regularly for students in order to extend their learning beyond the classroom whilst also promoting key life skills, such as taking responsibility and becoming organised. Indeed, in the EEF 'Teaching and Learning toolkit' (2021), homework is rated highly in terms of its potential educational impact.

The EEF explains that, when well designed, the use of homework can have a positive outcome on student progress (2021). Their recommendations include quality over quantity (less is more) and ensuring that the purpose of the homework is clear to students – it should integrate with classroom learning so as not to appear tokenistic. The impact can be furthered when paired with the receipt of 'high-quality feedback' (EEF, 2021). Remember, this does not have to be written but could be verbal or peer-based, such as a classroom discussion or question and answer. It is particularly worth noting that where additional resources such as home-learning clubs are also available, homework can benefit disadvantaged students (EEF, 2021).

Homework can sometimes become obsolete. It might be set in a rush at the end of the lesson so that students are not clear on what it involves, or perhaps wasn't planned for schematically, so that it acts as an 'add on' because it needed to be given. Given the positive impact it can have, seek to plan for homework in the same way you would your lesson, with a view to purpose, progress and inclusivity within a broader sequence of learning. Ensure that it feeds into future lessons so that students will have the opportunity to share and receive feedback on what they have done. Where possible, don't set homework as the last part of a lesson when time might be stretched. Instead, look to give it at a point when students can engage with what is being asked, the teacher can give a clear explanation of its requirements and students can ask questions as required.

Teachers' Standards 4 specifies the setting of homework as an opportunity to 'consolidate and extend the knowledge and understanding pupils have acquired' (DfE, 2021a, p. 11) and your reflections on the next page can be used as evidence towards this.

Reflections

Consider how you plan and set homework activities. Choose a piece you have set this week for a class and review it against the EEF criteria:

- Does it focus on quality over quantity?

- Was the purpose of the homework clearly communicated with students?

- Was it integrated into lesson learning?

- Was an opportunity provided for feedback of some description?

- Did you account for the needs of disadvantaged students, e.g. if it involved the use of technology were allowances made for those who might not have access to this at home?

Following your evaluation, consider the strengths in the homework you have set and where you might look to make further tweaks to maximise impact in line with the EEF evidence-based recommendations.

2, 4, 5, 6
TS

Favourite student quote

"

"

Highlight of the week

Week 4
Making use of technology

The use of technology in education is an area which has rapidly advanced in recent years. It is worth exploring how technology can help with protecting teacher time and assisting with student learning. For example, can you use a visualiser to mark an example piece of work in front of the class, modelling where improvements could be made or where marks can be awarded (DfE, 2019b, p. 5)? Is there a platform you can utilise to set a carefully-designed multiple-choice quiz so that you can gain an immediate insight from every student on their learning and understanding without having to look through a whole class set of work (DfE, 2019b, p. 5)? Are there subject-specific websites which can provide useful starting points for the setting of homework? When used well, technology can effectively

Reflections

On a scale of one to ten, with ten being incredibly confident, where would you rate yourself with the use of technology and its role in education? Which areas would you still like to learn about and who could you speak to or collaborate with at school in your planning to assist with this progress? Have you received training on your school's chosen platform or package? If not, flag this with your mentor so that they can assist accordingly. Reflect here on what steps you have already taken or might take to enhance your technology skill set.

Favourite student quote

" "

Highlight of the week

★

2, 4

TS

improve your wellbeing by reducing workload whilst simultaneously maintaining a focus on progress for all students. However, always be mindful of student access and resources, particularly if technology is required to complete a task as homework.

Think piece 9
Cognitive load

Have you ever taught a lesson where you felt students were not able to take in all the content? Perhaps there was too much information, the explanation was fast paced, or both? Cognitive load theory, a term associated with the research of John Sweller and associates, can help explain why.

Sweller explains that a school's role is to teach what evolutionary psychologist David Geary has termed 'biologically secondary knowledge'. 'Biologically primary knowledge' is skills and information that we acquire as part of life whilst 'secondary knowledge' is subject related and requires explicit instruction (Sweller, 2019, pp. 14–15). The process of learning secondary knowledge involves the working memory engaging with new information to acquire the relevant skills and knowledge so that these can be transposed into the long-term memory.

Sweller explains that by recognising the limits of the working memory and reducing the amount of processing required at any one time, the instructional expert (i.e. the teacher) assists the novice (i.e. the student) in increasing the amount of knowledge which can be accumulated by the long-term memory in what are termed 'schemas'. The long-term memory is not subject to the same limits as the working memory. It is therefore in the long-term memory that some of the necessary knowledge for processing this new secondary knowledge will already be stored in schemas (Sweller, 2019, pp. 15–17).

This lends itself to a series of instructional recommendations for trial in the classroom, which includes ensuring that there is adequate lesson pacing for allowing students to engage and process the taught material. Don't rush or try to cram in too much, and pair this with high-quality explanation and scaffolding. Signpost and clarify where there are synoptic links between new knowledge and prior learning to facilitate recall. Create chances for students to regularly apply and practice key skills (Tindall-Ford et al., 2019, p. 147).

Such techniques are summarised by David Didau as 'explicit instruction', central to reducing cognitive load (2019, p. 149). Didau suggests regularly revisiting specific key ideas within a curriculum to assist with student understanding and to cement long-term recall. Don't assume that students will learn through struggle. Instead, ensure that there is initial clarity with a success criterion so that students can then gradually internalise accurate knowledge through practice. This should be paired with the use of 'concrete examples' to clarify complex ideas and draw on visual imagery or diagrams to support accompanying explanations. Conversely, over-complicated text or unnecessary additional image use can have the reverse effect and overwhelm students' working memory – an example could include getting students to engage with information on a slide at the same time as listening to you (Didau, 2019, pp. 150–154).

Reflections

Past planning

Reflect on what steps you might have already taken to reduce cognitive load in the classroom. List here any strategies or techniques you have deployed which you have found to be particularly successful.

Preparation

Consider which of the recommendations to reduce cognitive load you might want to trial in lessons. Observe a member of staff who has strong practice in this area. Give examples of how you deployed the strategy/strategies in the classroom and how this was informed by your observation.

Follow-up

Evaluate how effectively you felt these strategies worked. How could you continue to promote this classroom practice?

2, 3, 4, 5
TS

Week 5
Use of group work

Teaching can be tiring at times, particularly after a day of multiple classes, possibly back-to-back, a difficult lesson or a challenging situation. It is why taking a break, such as having lunch with colleagues, is so essential for ensuring you have some rest and a chance to relax. As well as using personal time to feel refreshed, it can be helpful to consider how you can teach to improve both your energy levels and student learning. The Classroom Practice section of the ECF points out how, when designed carefully, group work can aid student progress (DfE, 2019a, p. 16) with the additional benefit of changing the dynamic and pace of the lesson.

'Collaborative Cognitive Load Theory' (CCLT) is posited by Zambrano et al. as a theoretical model that working together aids 'collective working memory', reducing individual cognitive load (2019, p. 31). They explain that essential to this is planning group sizes and compositions to ensure that there is a spectrum of individual knowledge which can be brought to a task. Instruction and scaffolding are also key here to ensure students can work, communicate and collaborate effectively together, remaining focused on the required activity. With experience and practice, the level of support can gradually be withdrawn (Zambrano et al., 2019, pp. 32–33).

It is worth considering if and how you make use of group work. The use of carefully-designed seating plans will help with ensuring appropriate group composition. Also, make sure you provide the same clarity with instruction and necessary support as you would with any other activity. Examples might include sentence stems to help structure discussions, assigning different members of the group a specific contribution point or roles, or giving a broken-down series of steps to complete the given task. This can then provide you with a valuable opportunity to move away from front-of-class teaching and circulate.

Reflections

Think about how you plan and use group work. Look ahead to a lesson where it will be required and reflect on how you can look to promote 'collective working memory' by considering group size and composition, and what instruction and scaffolding you can provide. Following the lesson, evaluate the activity and consider where you might look to make further tweaks to maximise impact.

Favourite student quote

"

"

Highlight of the week

Week 6
Revisiting appraisal targets (2)

This is your final week before the Easter holiday, and whilst it is a shorter term, the intensity of the Spring term means you may be feeling in need of a break. As always, plan to use the holiday to rest from work and to have activities to look forward to – you have earned this time off and deserve to relax and recuperate. Don't forget your out-of-office response on emails! With two-thirds of the academic year behind you (well done!), now is also an excellent opportunity to revisit your appraisal targets. Use the written record from your professional progress review to guide your notes. What successes do you feel proudest of? Which areas of the Teachers' Standards do you still need to evidence? What elements of the ECF might you benefit from further engagement with? What steps might you take to meet these recommendations? The evidence you have collated in this journal should also help to inform your continued steps for professional development.

Reflections

Return to your appraisal targets in the targets table on page 14 and update these in line with your most recent progress review using the questions on the previous page to prompt your thinking. Ensure that you continue to complete your Teachers' Standards table and use this to guide your future progress.

Reflect on your wellbeing across this term – have you felt overstressed at all and if so, what has caused it? Looking ahead and drawing on your reflections from this year, are there techniques or strategies you could deploy which would help to reduce these concerns? Make a note of any points you might want to raise with your mentor at your next meeting after the Easter break.

Finally, the end of term is an essential time to check in with your sense of wellbeing. If there are points where you felt particularly stressed, try to identify what factors contributed to this and how far they could be ameliorated in the future. Remember, teaching should be enjoyable and the accompanying workload feasible – if either of these no longer feel true to your experience then it is time to reach out to your mentor so that the appropriate support can be provided. This is not something to worry about, rather it shows strength of character, allowing you to develop long-term systems that will hopefully enable you to continue to flourish in the profession without burning out.

Favourite student quote

"

"

Highlight of the week

Now set out and plan what steps you can take to relax and unwind from work this holiday.

8

TS

Summer
term 1

Week 1
Reflecting on highlights

Welcome to the final term of your year as an ECT! Look back at the highlights and student quotes you have collated from across the weeks. Whilst there are always challenges within the profession, hopefully you have found being in the classroom and working with the young people in your care the extraordinary experience that it can be.

This term tends to be more relaxed as Years 11 and 13 leave for examinations and the end of term approaches. Continue to maintain your rigour in terms of classroom expectations and focus on pedagogy – learning must remain the priority. Remember to maintain standards, celebrate successes and continue to hold students to account whilst also

Reflections

Reflect on how far you have come since September. What have you enjoyed the most about your job so far this year? In what area are you proudest of your achievements?

relishing the knowledge that the long summer holiday is not too far away now! Use this to help you continue to find the energy required to be the best teacher you can be –you will only thank yourself later. A positive way of re-establishing expectations is by emphasising the many positive behaviours and engagement which have been demonstrated by students across the last term, using your school achievement system as appropriate.

Favourite student quote

❝

❞

Highlight of the week

Return to the guidance and reflections from Autumn 1, Weeks 1 and 2. Are there any further amendments required to your seating plans based on your experiences? Have you continued to welcome students at the door and present the best possible version of yourself? Have you maintained the expectations (including routines) that you communicated? If you haven't, that's ok, the key is to recognise this and consider how you can revisit these with your classes. This includes reinforcing all the positive behaviours which have been demonstrated in line with your classroom values by openly celebrating these successes with your classes and at home.

Week 2
Teaching lessons outside your subject area

As an ECT, you will have a reduced timetable. The guidance stipulates no more than 90 per cent for Year 1 and 95 per cent for Year 2, in addition to the PPA time all teachers are entitled to (DfE, 2021b, p. 15). Your timetable will be comprised of your subject classes but there may be times, either now or in the future, where you are required to teach a lesson or class that is not part of your schedule. This could include having to assist with departmental or tutorial cover arrangements, or, for some schools, teachers are part of a timetabled pastoral curriculum provision such as Personal, Social, Health and Economic education lessons (PSHEe) and/or Citizenship. Whatever the circumstance, this can be daunting for an ECT but please be reassured that it is not unusual to feel nervous at having to take a session with a new group or to teach a lesson outside of your usual domain.

The key is to utilise the same strategies you would with your teaching groups, including clarity of expectations and then consistency and fairness with the application of these. Equally, it is about ensuring you continue to deliver the same high-quality teaching and learning so that all students are able to access and therefore engage with the lesson content.

However, as always, it is important to stay mindful of your wellbeing. Don't be afraid to request additional support either in your preparations or with leading the class. You are perfectly entitled to this. Also note that the current Department for Education guidance stipulates that an institution should not 'normally demand teaching outside the age range and/or subject(s) for which the ECT has been employed to teach' (2021b, p. 15). If you have concerns in this respect, be honest and speak with your induction tutor.

Notes

Reflections

How would you feel being asked to cover or teach a lesson outside your allocated classes? What steps might you take to help prepare yourself for this both before and during the lesson? Make reference to your support network. Have you had any experiences that you could draw on in your reflections here?

1, 7, 8
TS

Favourite student quote

"

"

Highlight of the week

Think piece 10
Adaptive teaching

The ECF (DfE, 2019a, p.17) and Teachers' Standards 5 (DfE, 2021a, p. 11) both refer to 'adaptive teaching' – ensuring that teaching and learning is tailored to students' needs so that a fully inclusive offer is provided. This doesn't mean lowering academic expectations for some but rather ensuring that there is appropriate challenge for all.

To close the advantage gap, excellent pedagogy should be made available to all students, at all starting points (Didau, 2019, p. 163); Quigley and Coleman state that the effective use of oracy in the classroom has shown to be particularly beneficial to those from a disadvantaged background (2018, p. 26). Indeed, one piece of research suggests that high-quality teaching can have a lifetime impact on reducing disadvantage (Chetty et al., 2014). This means knowing your students as individuals and drawing on a range of best practice to teach for all, rather than seeing inclusion as an addition.

In terms of SEND, the same principles apply. Don't be guided by labels alone when determining requirements. The National Association for Special Educational Needs (nasen) has an excellent resource site for educational professionals. This includes guidance on best practice with a 'graduated approach' (2014). This starts with staff and SENCO liaising to ensure that there is a full assessment and thus understanding of a child's needs. In secondary schools, this could be communicated via a SEND register. This then allows the teacher to plan accordingly to meet those requirements. These strategies are then reviewed to measure impact. Teachers are encouraged to continue communications with all relevant specialist staff (nasen, 2014, pp. 6–13).

One important element is how teachers work with teaching assistants. In 2018, the EEF published a report into how teaching assistants could be used most effectively in the classroom (Sharples et al., 2018). They put forward a working principle that they should 'supplement, not replace the teacher' (2018, p. 14). It is essential that a teaching assistant should not be seen as the teacher of the students they care for – high-quality teaching is fully inclusive and thus it remains the teacher's responsibility to support those with SEND appropriately (2018, p. 13). To make the most effective use of your additional staff, communicate effectively the material and plans to be taught in advance of the lesson. Collaborate on how the teaching assistant can best support with the scaffolding of tasks for those with specific needs but with the same pedagogical aims of promoting independence with learning. Another tip is to encourage the teaching assistant to 'rove' around the classroom to provide a 'teaching triage', flagging where further help may be required to the teacher (2018, pp. 13-16).

Reflections

Past planning

When planning for your lessons, have you been aware of the diversity of needs within your class, including disadvantaged students, EAL, prior attainment and SEND? How have you sought to adapt your teaching to meet these needs to guarantee an inclusive offer? How have you made use of a teaching assistant in the classroom?

Preparation

Drawing on the guidance on the previous page, consider how you could look to promote outcomes for all students in your classroom by adapting your teaching accordingly. An observation or discussion with a more experienced member of staff would be recommended here. Include planning for how you could continue to maximise the effect of a teaching assistant's support in the classroom. If you haven't already, reading Chapter 6 from the Department for Education's *SEND code of practice: 0 to 25 years* is a helpful starting point.

Follow-up

Return here to evaluate the effectiveness of the steps you took to adapt your teaching and to promote inclusion. This should include a consideration of how you looked to collaborate effectively with the teaching assistant to best support the needs of the students.

Week 3
Coaching

This year, you will have had a mentor who has guided you through your first induction year as an ECT. However, looking ahead, you may want to also consider the option of having a coach. What's the difference? In the 'Pivotal Podcast' series (2020), Professor Rachel Lofthouse from Leeds Beckett University discussed her work on mentoring and coaching. Lofthouse recognised that the distinction is not always clear but suggests that in the context of education it can broadly be understood that a mentor's role is more instructive, 'driving an individual towards a set of standards', whilst a coach is facilitative. Coaches answer questions with questions, getting you to recognise your own knowledge, skills and strengths and how these can be deployed to improve your own practice and progress for students. A key feature of quality coaching is that you are paired with someone who has expertise in the area you are interested in developing. When deployed effectively, coaching can lead to teacher efficacy and sustainable quality practice (Lofthouse, 2020).

As you prepare for your formal review with your mentor, this might be a point for discussion as you look ahead to continuing your progression. Perhaps there is a specific area of your practice you feel would benefit from tailored support or an area of the ECF framework that you would still like to explore further as you continue to develop your classroom expertise. A coach is always a helpful resource at any point in your educational career as part of a journey of constant self-development, so don't hesitate to ask if it interests you.

Notes

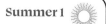

Reflections

Reflect on how a coach might help you develop your own practice further as an addition to your induction mentor – is there a specific area you would be interested in focusing on? Use these reflections as a basis for action planning your future development at your formal review.

**Favourite
student quote**

"

"

**Highlight
of the week**

★

8

TS

Week 4
Managing emails

In Autumn 2, Week 2, you mapped out how you use your time across a working week. One element of this is making certain that you keep organised with your emails, an integral part of a school's communication system. The email platform your school operates with will have built-in systems to help manage the demands of staying organised. Some examples might include flagging by urgency requests which need to be followed up, setting a reminder for when a request is due and filtering into folders if you need to return to a particular message. In terms of the emails you send, always consider if it is possible to have a conversation with the relevant member of staff instead. As well as being easier and quicker, it can help reduce the flow of email traffic and often aids clarity in communications.

How you manage your emails interlinks with staff wellbeing. Your school is likely to already have

Reflections

Return to Autumn 2, Week 2 for a reminder of a strategy for organising your working week to promote efficiency and time management. Have you continued to use it to help organise your working week? Are there additional techniques you have made use of? Reflect on what steps you can continue to take to assist you with managing your workload.

guidance in place around email protocols but points to consider include setting limits on when you check or send emails, particularly outside the working day. Reading an email at home which causes undue anxiety or concern can be difficult and if you had received the same email in school you would have the necessary support network in place to help resolve or talk through the particular issue raised. For this reason, limit the hours you check your emails and don't be tempted to have them easily accessible on your phone – this constant access denies you the break from work which is required at weekends and evenings.

Favourite student quote

66

99

Highlight of the week

Track when and how much time you spend on your emails across a working week. Where might you want to draw boundaries to promote wellbeing? For example, do you need to look at emails outside of the school day? Next, look at the emails you sent. Are there any that might have been helped with a conversation instead? Finally, how confident do you feel managing your inbox? Is there anyone you might want to speak to for further support and guidance here?

Use these reflections to action plan next steps for managing your emails to promote efficiency and organisation whilst protecting your time and promoting work/life boundaries.

Think piece 11
Dialogic talk and questioning

Robin Alexander's seminal text *Towards Dialogic Teaching* (2004) sought to recentre high-quality classroom talk as an essential feature of strong classroom practice, with research suggesting that it can improve children's development psychologically, sociologically, and cognitively (2004, pp. 7–11). Alexander argues that effective classroom talk can be identified by several key features and that teachers should seek to envelop these aims within their planning. Talk between students and teachers is collaborative: this means conversations are responsive, building on each other's questions or ideas to create new areas of thought. This leads to a productive environment where students feel safe discussing and sharing their points (2004, pp. 22–23).

Arguably, an integral element of this is the use of questions. Rosenshine suggests that a practitioner who can make use of effective, regular questioning can gain a clearer understanding of student's learning (2010, pp. 12, 18). Essential here is the quality of the questions asked. For example, utilising them as an opportunity to review prior learning to cement knowledge in the long-term memory. There should also be an onus on the answering individual to justify their conclusions (Rosenshine, 2010, p. 18). Wiliam flags several effective techniques, including deploying what he terms 'no hands up except to ask a question' (2018, p. 93). This means embedding a practice of 'wait-time' after questioning, and allowing the possibility to discuss with a peer first (2018, pp. 96–97). This should then give scope for the teacher to select any student to answer, giving a key insight into their learning whilst simultaneously maintaining the classroom expectation that all must participate.

This opportunity to utilise 'accountable talk' in the classroom can consolidate curriculum knowledge as well as improve literary outcomes, specifically oracy skills (Quigley & Coleman, 2018, p. 29). Quigley and Coleman advise that promoting oracy excellence involves supporting students in understanding how they can justify their arguments through a reasoning process and being clear with expectations and ground rules around speaking conduct (2018, p. 27). This requires careful scaffolding from the professional to ensure that students can access the demands of the given task – this might include oracy sentence starters or modelling (2018, p. 29).

Reflections

Past planning

Reflect on how far you promote collaborative, accountable talk in the classroom, both in terms of questions and discussion work. What scaffolding do you provide to support this? Which strategies or techniques have you deployed that you have found to be particularly successful?

Preparation

Consider which of the recommendations on the previous page you might want to make more use of in lessons. Can you conduct an observation of a member of staff who has strong practice in this area? Give examples of how you incorporated the strategy/strategies into your classroom practice and how this was informed by your observation.

Follow-up

Evaluate how effectively you felt these strategies worked. For example, did your use of wait time allow students to answer who might not have previously? Did your additional scaffolding or modelling allow for a stronger justification of student answers? How could you continue to promote these classroom practices?

4

TS

Week 5
Curriculum planning for the future

It is at this point in the academic year that you may be starting to look ahead and plan for the future. You might be considering where schemes of work and curriculum content you have taught could be altered or improved, drawing on your reflections. Refer to Autumn 2, Week 3 and Think piece 4 (Subject and curriculum knowledge) to remind yourself how working with more experienced colleagues when curriculum planning can both improve student progress and staff workloads. Now is an excellent opportunity to speak to your mentor and/or Head of Department about your ideas for future plans and to enter into a collaborative, creative process with colleagues during available shared time to make the necessary edits. This helps to spread the work whilst also allowing for multiple perspectives to have an input with a focus on best pedagogy.

Reflections

Reflect on your planning from this year. Are there any specific units you would like to improve? Why? Be clear that the rationale is to benefit student learning. Then use this as the starting point for your conversation with your mentor or Head of Department this week to consider where collaborative planning might help to inform this work. Record your next steps here.

Draw on your experiences from this year along with your work in this journal's Think pieces to consider where you can schematically plan to challenge misconceptions, embed domain-specific metacognitive tasks, include practice retrieval testing, and so forth. It is also important to remember that change should be incremental so don't seek to overhaul everything, rather prioritise and be specific with your focus. Remember, you are the most important resource in the classroom, the materials only supplement your delivery so don't create hours of work for yourself.

Favourite student quote

"

"

Highlight of the week

★

★

3, 4

Week 6
Half-termly reflections (3)

The end of the first summer half-term is already here. In Autumn 2, Week 4 we discussed the importance of parent, carer and guardian communication as an essential link in the relationship between school, professional and student. Why not now end this term with some positive messages home? It allows you to continue to both reinforce and promote your classroom expectations whilst also deservedly recognising those exceptional individuals who consistently surpass these. Focus on progress or effort here rather than outcomes.

Conversely, where there are more difficult calls to make, remember to stay focused on the choices being made by the student rather than anything which is personal. Always explain to the individual

---

Reflections

Consider how continuing to maintain lines of communication with home, including the celebration of successes, helps you to maintain and consolidate your classroom expectations. Can you give an example from your most recent experiences?

_____

_____

_____

_____

Reflect on this half-term with a focus on teaching and learning, professional development and wellbeing. What has gone well? Has it developed as you thought? What might you want to do differently next half-term?

• **Teaching and learning**

_____

_____

_____

Favourite student quote

"

"

how their behaviours can change to meet expectations – you don't want them to feel 'written off'. Remember to be a model of the language and manners that you want to see in the classroom.

Finally, with the half-term holiday and your formal assessment ahead, take some time to complete your reflections and then plan for your week off focusing on self-care.

Highlight of the week

- **Professional development**

- **Wellbeing**

The half-term week is time for some much-needed self-care. List three treats you are going to give yourself this half-term holiday and ensure that you stick to these regardless of other commitments – you have absolutely earned them!

1.

2.

3.

1, 7, 8

TS

Summer
term 2

Week 1
Preparation for formal assessment

You are now into your final half-term. The weather is warmer, the daylight hours longer and you should deservedly feel a positive sense of achievement at how much you have learnt and progressed as a professional across this year.

As this is your last half-term, you will be looking to finalise your evidence in preparation for your formal assessment with your induction tutor. Remember, you shouldn't have to create material specifically for this but rather be collating what you already have, including that which you gathered for your progress reviews (DfE, 2021b, p. 22). The guidance stipulates that 'there is no need for the ECT to create anything new for the formal assessment, they should draw from their work as a teacher and from their induction programme' (DfE, 2021b, p. 22).

The Teachers' Standards table in this journal will help direct you to

Reflections

Ensure that you have updated your Teachers' Standards table with notes of any additional relevant evidence you have collated.

Return to your appraisal targets from your last progress review. How have you moved forward with these? Use your Teachers' Standard table and your reflections from this journal to detail below any further preparations you need to take for your formal assessment. Remember, if you are feeling anxious to draw on the wellbeing resources detailed in Spring 2, Week 2.

how your reflections evidence your practice in fulfilling these. It is also worth noting that at this assessment 'there should be nothing unexpected' (DfE, 2021b, p. 22) as you will have been consistently reviewing your performance through your professional progress reviews and conversations with your mentor and induction tutor. This means that you should try not to feel unduly concerned or anxious about your formal assessment. Instead, reframe it as an opportunity to celebrate your hard work and progress and to continue to receive the support you are entitled to in order to move forward in your professional practice.

Favourite student quote

"

"

Highlight of the week

Think piece 12
Literacy

All educators, regardless of their subject, should see themselves as teachers of literacy. Willingham writes that reading is integral to the acquisition of knowledge and therefore student outcomes (2009, p. 37). So, it is not a surprise that evidentially the 'literacy gap' between students impacts on how far individuals can successfully access the secondary curriculum (Quigley & Coleman, 2018, p. 6). For example, Quigley sets out what he terms the 'arduous eight', a summary of the multiple challenges which can face a student when they seek to access a specific school text (2020, p. 51). These include length, the language used, structure, an assumption of implicit background or cultural understanding, and inclusion or lack thereof of any additional explanatory support within the writing. He argues that this is often paired with young people who do not have the skills or processes in place to tackle these difficulties (Quigley & Coleman, 2018, p. 52).

To combat this, Quigley and Coleman's EEF report 'Improving literacy in secondary schools' (2018) emphasises the responsibility of all teachers to develop literate students within their subject area, termed 'disciplinary literacy' (2018, p. 7). For example, making the structure of a domain text explicit, utilising a textbook glossary (Quigley, 2020, pp. 62, 66) or helping students to understand how and why an academic in your subject area would write, read or talk in a specific way (Quigley & Coleman, 2018, p. 7).

Vocabulary is just as essential: language which should be explicitly explained to students within a curriculum discipline. One model distinguishes here between Tier 2 and Tier 3. Tier 2 can be broadly defined as words used frequently in multiple contexts across subject areas such as 'analyse', whilst Tier 3 are subject-specific terms, for example 'osmosis' in science. Classroom teaching should include deploying strategies which help with accessing and remembering the contents of these terms, such as breaking down the origins or making use of visual aids (Quigley & Coleman, 2018, p. 12). This exposure to key terms will then further assist with the use of classroom reading strategies whereby academic texts can be broken down. This means giving students opportunities to clarify and question elements they are uncertain about and to explicitly draw upon subject-specific areas, such as context or source, to further aid understanding (Quigley & Coleman, 2018, pp. 18–19).

Utilising reading effectively in this respect will also arguably improve performance with written work as students continue to gain an understanding of what successful academic work can look like within your subject domain (Quigley & Coleman, 2018, p. 22). This can be assisted further with the use of scaffolding and modelling when completing written tasks which should include 'planning, drafting and editing stages' (Quigley & Coleman, 2018, p. 21).

Reflections

Past planning

Reflect on how far your planning and delivery of learning provides for literate needs including reading, vocabulary and writing. Which strategies or techniques have you found to be particularly successful?

Preparation

Consider which of the recommendations on the previous page you might want to make more use of in lessons. Begin by ensuring that you are aware of the individual requirements within your classes – reading ages data can provide one helpful measure here. Consider where you might benefit from additional support with disciplinary literacy, e.g. shared planning or observation of a colleague within your department. Give examples of how you utilised the strategy/strategies to teach literacy in the classroom.

Follow-up

Evaluate how effectively you felt these strategies worked. For example, were students able to better access a piece of academic reading to make use of Tier 2 or 3 vocabulary or to complete an element of academic writing? If you met with a colleague, what did you learn from this? How could you continue to promote this classroom practice?

2, 3, 5
TS

Week 2
Looking ahead to end-of-term celebrations

If you teach exam classes you might have gained some time and, with only a few weeks left, your workload may have now reduced. Continue to prioritise high-quality teaching and learning but don't be afraid to leave earlier than you usually would at the end of the working day if you can. Equally, now is an excellent time to look to organise a social with colleagues, especially your fellow ECTs. You deserve to celebrate the close of an important year and this journal is testament to your growth.

With the end of term approaching, consider how far you have managed to continue any hobbies or activities that you enjoy during this year. It could be reading a book, exercising or spending time with friends. If work has become too dominant, consider what adjustment can be made so that

Reflections

Looking ahead to the end of term, can you agree a date now with your other ECT colleagues to celebrate the end of your induction year? Also, make a plan with your out-of-school support network to celebrate the end of this academic year and your achievements as an ECT. Write down the details of what you will do and when.

Favourite student quote

"

"

you can plan in protected time for these activities as you look ahead to the next academic year. If you cannot see how it is possible, then speak to your mentor at your next meeting about this so that together you can scrutinise your workload and working patterns to alleviate some time across a week.

Highlight of the week

Reflect on the activities you enjoy beyond your job and how far you have been able to undertake these this year. Looking ahead, are there any adjustments you feel you need to make to ensure that you have time to relax and engage with these hobbies beyond working hours? Record your plans here.

Week 3
Future Continuing Professional Development (CPD)

Your formal assessment is a chance to consider your progress from this past year. This week is an opportunity to look ahead to your focus points for next year. As part of their investment in staff development, schools will provide whole-staff learning opportunities and training. However, it may be that at this point there is a specific area that you feel would benefit you as the next step of your professional journey. This could relate to an element of curriculum practice, an additional responsibility that you would be interested in preparing for, or it might be that you want to become more involved in an area of the school's provision. Having the discussion with your mentor this side of the summer holiday helps with planning ahead for how you could be supported in this.

Reflections

You have now engaged with all the pedagogical Think pieces in this journal. Using your reflections and the Teachers' Standards table to guide you, which area of techniques or strategies might you specifically want to revisit for further growth?

Favourite student quote

"

"

For example, it might be arranging to shadow a colleague, looking to have a coach for the Autumn term, arranging a meeting with a member of staff, or attending an external provider's course.

Highlight of the week

★

★

Use your reflections from this year to guide your planning for professional development next year. What might you want to focus on and why? What support would help you with this? Follow up your reflections with details of the arrangements you make.

8

TS

Week 4
Preparing for the Autumn term

You are nearing the end of term and are hopefully looking forward to your long, and well-deserved, summer holiday. At this time in the year, it can feel difficult to think ahead to Autumn and the start of a new academic year. However, you are likely to have some more time at present, so if there is preparation you can complete now then your future self will feel very grateful when you return from your summer break and meet the demands of the new school term. It could be as simple as organising some resources or making tweaks to a scheme of learning in readiness for teaching in the new term.

As far as possible, don't plan to complete work over the summer holiday, particularly if it could be done now. Remember that within a working week you are likely to

Reflections

Looking ahead to the start of the Autumn term, are there preparations required that you could complete now without creating an onerous workload? Be clear that your justifications for these are learning focused. List here what you would like to complete and when. If it is going to mean working beyond your usual hours then scrutinise your list to see if it can be reduced.

be more efficient and focused than when you are on holiday and operating at a different pace. You also need the holiday to unwind and relax so that you feel refreshed when you return in the Autumn term.

If you want to help prepare for the return towards the end of the holiday, then learning from educational research can be both enjoyable and beneficial. A helpful starting point could be the *Great Teaching Toolkit Evidence Review* (Coe et al., 2020). Rooted in research, this accessible document also overlaps with much of the ECF.

Favourite student quote

"

"

Highlight of the week

★

★

Week 5
Planning for wellbeing

This journal has hopefully allowed you to record your journey as a practitioner but has also reminded you how important it is to maintain a focus on your wellbeing. Ultimately, in the pressurised job of teaching, self-care must be prioritised to avoid burnout. You need to have boundaries with your work/life balance. This means working 'smart' by deploying strategies that allow you to be efficient and organised but also to maintain lines of communication with your in-school support network, being honest and open when your workload has become too much.

Using your experiences and reflections from this year, look ahead to the next academic year to consider how you will continue to look after yourself. You could consider setting up or joining a wellbeing group for you and your fellow ECTs, a monthly cake club or just ensure that there are chances to meet regularly and share effective strategies. Having this support in place will help you to maintain that essential network for self-care as you start the next academic year.

You might also be interested to know that in 2021 the government published 'The Education Staff Wellbeing Charter' (DfE, 2021d), a set of commitments around promoting positive mental health that have been put forward by the Department for Education and OFSTED. It includes a series of recommendations for educational institutes which they are invited to sign up to.

Notes

Reflections

Write down the strategies or techniques that you have found most effective this year for helping to maintain your wellbeing – the reflections in this journal will help guide you. The strategies could be in-school, e.g. a revised approach to planning or marking, or at home, e.g. with a cut-off time for working, a 'no-email' time zone or ensuring you have something enjoyable booked in for holiday time. Use these to guide your wellbeing action points for next year.

Favourite student quote

"

"

Highlight of the week

Week 6
Reflections and advice for future ECTs

As you come to the end of the academic year, this is an important opportunity to reflect on your efforts and the progress you have made. Part of the aim of this journal is to help empower you to enjoy the teaching profession and to find strategies which promote great practice whilst also enabling you to remain disciplined with your working hours. The education sector needs to retain individuals such as yourself, and your growth this year can be an inspiration for other teachers starting out in the profession.

This week is a chance to think about how far you have come and to consider what key advice you want to remember in September. However, this same advice might also be something you would want to share with any first-year ECTs starting at your institution in the Autumn. To meet and hear from a colleague who has completed the year can be an aspirational source of reassurance for new ECTs, and you are uniquely placed to share insights from your own experiences.

Start with your preparations for meeting your classes in the Autumn term. Did the research you undertook provide you with the required insight? How were your seating plans? Then consider when you met your groups. Were your expectations clear and were you able to create a mutually respectful, trusting classroom culture? Have your expectations changed across this year and if so, how and why? What have been your experiences with behaviour management and what techniques have you found to be most effective? In terms of quality of teaching and learning, review the core principles covered in the ECF. What strategies have you found helpful for deploying key pedagogical theory in the classroom?

Notes

Reflections

Using the questions on the previous page as a starting point, write down five pieces of advice you would like to remember for yourself in the new Autumn term, drawing on your experiences this year. Speak to your induction tutor about the possibility of sharing these with the new ECT cohort when they arrive in the next academic year.

1.

2.

3.

4.

5.

Favourite student quote

"

"

Highlight of the week

★

Week 7
Congratulations!

Huge congratulations on completing your first year as an ECT. If you can, spend some time this week looking back through this journal – you should feel very proud. Your reflections show an individual who is dedicated to their profession, and one who is constantly seeking to learn and improve. This journal is testament to what you have already achieved and the resilience you have demonstrated.

You should feel empowered with the knowledge that your focus on student learning will have had a positive impact on all those young people you have educated in your classroom this year. Celebrate the successes as you read your weekly highlights and reflect on your favourite student quotes – they can help you feel excited for the year ahead as you continue your journey as a teacher, and give you the confidence that you are ready for the next step.

My vision is that this journal has helped you to understand that working in education doesn't have to be at the expense of your own wellbeing but that with effective strategies you can have a positive work/life balance. I also hope that it has shown you that the drive for self-improvement in teaching never ends and that a reflective practitioner always seeks ways to improve the impact they can have.

For now, enjoy this last week of term. Celebrate with your fellow ECTs and spend time with your colleagues. Plan a treat for the last day to recognise the momentous occasion of completing your ECT year and to mark the start of your holiday. Have a relaxing summer break with family and friends and return to the preparation sections of this journal to remind you that you do not need to be working during the summer holiday. Teaching is an incredibly rewarding profession; you have chosen a career where you are making a difference to the young people in your care every day. An outstanding holistic education opens a world of possible future pathways for students, allowing them to fulfil their hopes and ambitions. Thank you for choosing to be a part of this and I hope you will stay and excel within it for many years to come.

Reflections

Look back through your reflections in this journal. Read your weekly highlights, favourite student quotes, and look at your now completed Teachers' Standards table. Use these to complete three highlights of your year or points you are proudest of (more is also acceptable of course!). This could include something you have learnt, an area you have developed in or a happy memory.

At the end of this year, take some time to reflect on the values that have driven your work as a teacher. What is it that motivated you to enter the profession? How have your experiences this year helped to cement this? Are there any additional reasons you would now add? Use these to remind yourself of what you do and why, always with a view to best outcomes for all students.

Favourite student quote

"

"

Highlight of the week

★ Highlights of the year

Notes

Bibliography

Alexander, R. (2004), *Towards Dialogic Teaching: Rethinking Classroom Talk*. Cambridge: Dialogos.

Allison, S. and Tharby, A. (2015), *Making Every Lesson Count: Six principles to support great teaching and learning*. Carmarthen: Crown House.

Ashbee, R. (2021), *Curriculum: Theory, Culture and the Subject Specialisms*. Oxon: Routledge.

Bennett, T. and Berry, J. (2017), 'Behaviour', in C. Hendrick and R. Macpherson (eds), *What Does This Look Like in the Classroom? Bridging the Gap Between Research and Practice*. Woodbridge: John Catt Educational, pp. 49–62.

Chetty, R., Friedman, J. N. and Rockoff, J. E. (2014), 'Measuring the Impacts of Teachers II: Teacher Value-Added and Student Outcomes in Adulthood', *American Economic Review*, 104, (9), 2633–2679.

Coe, R., Rauch, C. J., Kime, S. and Singleton, D. (2020), 'Great Teaching Toolkit Evidence Review', *Evidence Based Education in partnership with Cambridge Assessment International Education*, https://assets.website-files com/5ee28729f7b4a5fa99bef2b3/5ee9f507021911ae35ac6c4d_EBE_GTT_EVIDENCE%20REVIEW_DIGITAL.pdf

Department for Education (2015), 'Special educational needs and disability code of practice: 0 to 25 years: statutory guidance for organisations which work with and support children and young people who have special educational needs or disabilities', https://assets.publishing.service.gov.uk/government/uploads/system/uploads/attachment_data/file/398815/SEND_Code_of_Practice_January_2015.pdf

Department for Education (2016), 'Eliminating unnecessary workload around marking: report of the independent teacher workload review group', https://assets.publishing.service.gov.uk/government/uploads/system/uploads/attachment_data/file/511256/Eliminating-unnecessary-workload-around-marking.pdf

Department for Education (2019a), 'Early Career Framework', https://assets.publishing.service.gov.uk/government/uploads/system/uploads/attachment_data/file/978358/Early-Career_Framework_April_2021.pdf

Department for Education (2019b), 'Ways to reduce workload in your school(s): tips and case studies from school leaders, teachers and sector experts', https://assets.publishing.service.gov.uk/government/uploads/system/uploads/attachment_data/file/838687/Tips_for_school_leaders_.pdf

Department for Education (2021a), 'Teachers' standards: guidance for school leaders, school staff and governing bodies', https://assets.publishing.service.gov.uk/government/uploads/system/uploads/attachment_data/file/1007716/Teachers__Standards_2021_update.pdf

Department for Education (2021b), 'Induction for early career teachers (England): statutory guidance for appropriate bodies, headteachers, school staff and governing bodies', https://assets.publishing.service.gov.uk/government/uploads/system/uploads/attachment_data/file/972316/Statutory_Induction_Guidance_2021_final__002____1__1_.pdf

Department for Education (2021c), 'Keeping children safe in education 2021: statutory guidance for schools and colleges', https://assets.publishing.service.gov.uk/government/uploads/system/uploads/attachment_data/file/1021914/KCSIE_2021_September_guidance.pdf

Department for Education (2021d), 'The Education Staff Wellbeing Charter', https://assets.publishing.service.gov.uk/government/uploads/system/uploads/attachment_data/file/1034032/DfE_Education_Workforce_Welbeing_Charter_Nov21.pdf

Didau, D. (2019), *Making Kids Cleverer: A Manifesto for Closing the Advantage Gap*. Carmarthen: Crown House.

Dix, P. (2017), *When the Adults Change, Everything Changes: Seismic Shifts in School Behaviour*. Carmarthen: Independent Thinking Press.

Dweck, C. (2017), *Mindset: Changing the way you think to fulfil your potential* (2nd edn). London: Robinson.

Education Endowment Foundation (2021), 'Teaching and Learning Toolkit', https://educationendowmentfoundation.org.uk/education-evidence/teaching-learning-toolkit

Fletcher-Wood, H. (2018), *Responsive Teaching: Cognitive Science and Formative Assessment in Practice*. Oxon: Routledge.

Lemov, D., Hernandez, J. and Kim, J. (2016), *Teach Like a Champion Field Guide 2.0: A Practical Resource to Make the 62 Techniques Your Own*. San Francisco: Jossey-Bass.

Lofthouse, R. (2020), *Coaching, mentoring – what's the difference? Rachel Lofthouse explains*. [Podcast]. 4 December 2019. Available at: http://www.pivotalpodcast.com/coaching-mentoring-whats-the-difference-rachel-lofthouse-explains-pp247/

Marzano, R. J. and Marzano, J. S. (2003), 'The key to classroom management' in *Educational Leadership*, 61, 6–13. Available at: https://www.ascd.org/el/articles/the-key-to-classroom-management

National Association for Special Educational Needs (2014), 'SEN Support and the Graduated Approach: A quick guide to ensuring that every child or young person gets the support they require to meet their needs', https://nasen-prod-asset.s3.eu-west-2.amazonaws.com/s3fs-public/sen support press 0.pdf

Perkins, D. (1992), *Smart Schools: From Training Memories to Educating Minds*. New York: Free Press.

Quigley, A. (2020), *Closing the Reading Gap*. Oxon: Routledge.

Quigley, A. and Coleman, R. (2018), 'Improving literacy in secondary schools', https://educationendowmentfoundation.org.uk/education-evidence/guidance-reports/literacy-ks3-ks4

Rosenshine, B. (2010), 'Principles of instruction', *Educational Practices Series*, 21, http://www.ibe.unesco.org/fileadmin/user_upload/Publications/Educational_Practices/EdPractices_21.pdf

Sharples, J., Webster, R. and Blatchford, P. (2018), 'Making Best Use of Teaching Assistants: Guidance Report', https://educationendowmentfoundation.org.uk/education-evidence/guidance-reports/teaching-assistants

Sherrington, T. (2019), *Rosenshine's Principles in Action*. Woodbridge: John Catt Educational.

Sweller, J. (2019), 'Cognitive Load Theory' in S. Tindall-Ford, S. Agostinho and J. Sweller (eds), *Advances in Cognitive Load Theory: Rethinking Teaching*. Oxon: Routledge, pp. 14–19.

Tindall-Ford, S., Agostinho, S. and Sweller J. (2019), 'Conclusions', in S. Tindall-Ford, S. Agostinho and J. Sweller (eds), *Advances in Cognitive Load Theory: Rethinking Teaching*. Oxon: Routledge, pp. 146–149.

Vygotsky, L. S. (1978), *Mind in Society: Development of Higher Psychological Processes*. London: Harvard University Press.

Wiliam, D. (2018), *Embedded Formative Assessment* (2nd edn). Bloomington: Solution Tree Press.

Wiliam, D. and Christodoulou, D. (2017), 'Assessment, marking & feedback', in C. Hendrick and R. Macpherson (eds), *What Does This Look Like In The Classroom? Bridging the Gap Between Research and Practice*. Woodbridge: John Catt Educational, pp. 22–48.

Willingham, D. T. (2009), *Why Don't Students Like School? A Cognitive Scientist Answers Questions About How the Mind Works and What It Means for the Classroom*. San Francisco: Jossey-Bass.

Wood, D., Bruner, J. and Ross, G. (1976), 'The role of tutoring in problem solving', *Journal of Child Psychology and Psychiatry*, 17, (2), 89–100.

Zambrano, J. R., Kirschner, A. P. and Kirschner, F. (2019), 'How Cognitive Load Theory Can Be Applied to Collaborative Learning: Collaborative Cognitive Load Theory', in S. Tindall-Ford, S. Agostinho and J. Sweller (eds), *Advances in Cognitive Load Theory: Rethinking Teaching*. Oxon: Routledge, pp. 30–35.